The Spirit of Herefordshire

The Spirit of Herefordshire

by
Jill Howard-Jones

Logaston Press

LOGASTON PRESS
Little Logaston Woonton Almeley
Herefordshire HR3 6QH

First published by Logaston Press 1994

ISBN 1 873827 14 8

Set in Times 11/13 pt by Logaston Press
and printed on Five Seasons Recycled Paper
in Great Britain by Ebenezer Baylis & Son, Worcester

For Peter and Paul

Geniumque loci primamque deorum
Tellurem Nymphasque et adhuc ignota precatur
Flumina

He prays to the spirit of the place and to Earth the first
of the gods and to the Nymphs and as yet unknown
rivers

Virgil. Aeneid vii

Contents

Acknowledgments

I am indebted to my publishers, Andy Johnson and Ron Shoesmith, for their support and guidance especially in checking historical details, to my husband, Ray, for his dedicated proof-reading and to Brian Byron for his splendid illustrations.

I am also particularly grateful to Joan Williams the Cathedral Librarian whose help in researching the background to my stories has been invaluable.

In addition I wish to record my grateful thanks to the following individuals and institutions: the Dean and Chapter of Hereford Cathedral; Robin Hill and his staff of the Hereford branch of the County Library; the Hereford branch of the County Record Office; Lady Hawkins School, Kington; Miss Meryl Jancey; Henry James and Egerton Parker of the History Department and Dick Rhodes of the Classics' Department of Hereford Cathedral School; the Historical Association; Friends of Ledbury Parish Church; Ledbury Tourist Information Office; the Curator of Leominster Museum; the Reverend Peter Privett of the Priory Church of St. Peter & St. Paul, Leominster; Anne Sandford, curator of Hereford City Museums; Chris Tobey of Brockhampton Court and Mrs. Charles G. Parkinson of Clifford Castle.

Introduction

Every village and market town in Herefordshire has its prevailing atmosphere, its own story to tell. But how can the spirit of such places be captured? And who can best capture it? Why not someone from the village's unique past, awaiting a voice and a characterisation true to the events, for historical accuracy must be preserved.

A dip into the past pulls Merewald from the mound at Kingsland where tradition has buried him, sets Godric Mapson on top of his castle keep at Goodrich, releases Rosamund Clifford to the arms of her royal lover, incites Tom Spring to bare his fists during the Fownhope Club Walk, prompts Adam de Orleton to murder his king, places Wulviva of Woolhope at the mercy of the Mordiford dragon, who has his own fiery tale to tell.

Local characters come alive and take me over, each telling his or her personal story within the framework of fact, for it could all have happened just as they tell it; who can prove otherwise? The place suddenly takes on a new life coloured by the personality of its narrator; whilst the known facts on which the story builds are given in the Sources at the end of the book.

For me it has been a way of re-discovering beautiful Herefordshire, seeing it through the eyes of those who lived here hundreds of years ago. I hope that readers, young and old, will have the same experience—and enjoy my stories, or rather stories of the spirits of the county.

Jill Howard-Jones
October 1994

Brother Edgar of Abbeydore

fter tending the sheep on the lonely hills, I'm suddenly thrust into the deafening hustle and bustle that surrounds the abbey gatehouse. There is so much activity. A cart loaded with logs clatters over the cobbles beneath the vaulted stone entrance while another loaded with beer barrels goes out. There are side doors for pedestrians on either side of the passage, but I still have a job to keep my balance with so many people pushing past.

I'm so slow compared to others. My legs are more bent and twisted than the apple trees in our orchards, where I can vouch for there being more thistles this year than last—and less dock leaves to soothe my stings when my legs give way and I fall in the nettles.

I am always falling but Brother Joseph tells me to bear my cross with fortitude. Bear it I do, for at Dore Abbey they have accepted me as a lay brother. The white-robed monks welcomed me. They took me in and gave me a home when I was orphaned and destitute. "'Be good to the poor!' say the Bells of Abbeydore,' and they've been good to me alright.

These monks have known poverty themselves. When they first arrived, they lived in rough wooden huts till, with the financial support of their founder,

Robert Fitz Harold of Ewyas, a grandson of William I, they were able to build their first abbey. They dedicated it to Our Lady of course—for Cistercians don't go in for cults and relics, just simple faith and building abbeys! The proof is here: just look at our abbey today, nearly a century later.

What's been achieved in this lush river valley, which leads from the rolling hills of Herefordshire up into the Black Mountains of Wales, is nothing short of miraculous. With their own hands they built this great abbey, hewn out of red sandstone. Now it stands with clusters of buildings around it: the great barn over 200 feet long and 40 feet wide, the malthouse, the granary, the stables—not forgetting the bakery, brewery, dovecot and smithy. All the needs of life are supplied within our precincts.

Yet this is a remote spot for that's what Cistercian monks like about it. They like wild places—away from the influence of worldly people. They do all the work themselves and refuse to employ servants, which is why I couldn't be one. So I'm a lay brother instead, though I'm not strong like the other lay brothers who cope with all the heavy labour, including the farm work. There is much to do—we have nearly 3,000 sheep out there on the hills. Our wool is in great demand, the most expensive wool in England. We have 54 cows too, and helping to milk them is one of my tasks. We lay brothers are children of the soil and artisans but we have made vows before the abbot like our spiritual brethren.

Admittedly, I'm better educated than most of the lay brothers for, when I was sick, Brother Joseph taught me to read and write. He's such a clever old monk, so skilled in making medicines and ointments from his herb garden. Travellers from the outside world come to him for advice and treatment and they pay well. The money goes towards further building projects for the abbey, to which my brethren are so committed.

That's the down side of being a lay brother: you can't escape the work! They talk of nothing else when they break silence. I know

3

because I lodge with the other lay brothers on the western side of the cloister. We use the lower storey by day and the upper storey as our dormitory at night.

I follow their general timetable too, of course, which is different to that of the choir monks like Brother Joseph. We have shorter services in church and more ample meals. As manual workers we eat flesh-meat, which the choir monks aren't allowed (alas, I have been persuaded to sell my meat secretly to a choir monk who shall be nameless), though they occasionally partake of fish from the river and dine off chicken and geese on feast days.

Choir monks aren't supposed to have large appetites, but lay brothers certainly have! I need less meat than the others because I do the less arduous jobs like bringing in the logs, tending the sheep and hoeing the weeds. The Cistercian Order relies on our manual labour. My brethren have done so much: from clearing the site, to laying out the gardens and fields and reclaiming the land—and then there's the building.

Believe me, lay brothers are always building—sometimes under the direction of top craftsmen brought in by the abbot to supervise the construction of the transepts and chapels. Skilled stone-masons who travelled about the country were accommodated in a nearby house that has become known as the masons' lodge. Master masons drew plans and directed the work. Eventually their extravagance incurred the abbot's displeasure and we monks took over. Inevitably, therefore, the building of the abbey tends to go in fits and starts.

'Why so many chapels?' I ask Brother Joseph. I can't understand why we need two chapels on the north side and another two on the south side and there are altars in the transepts too. 'Isn't that big altar table sufficient for all of us?' I persist.

He stirs the pungent concoction in the cooking pot over the fire as he replies, 'It is a rule of our order Edgar, my son, that each monk says Mass each day and so we need many altars. The Holy Sacrament is the living Body and Blood of Christ, my son. Do not forget that!'

I won't, for what I want more than anything (well not quite more than anything, because that would be to walk on straight legs) is to be a choir monk. Choir monks attend all the religious services in

4

addition to looking after the business matters and the reading and writing work of the monastery.

Never let it be said that choir monks at Dore forget their vows. I know that the learned Giraldus accuses them of avarice and lust in his *Speculum Ecclesie*! But Adam, a monk from our own abbey, has cleared the name of choir monks in the book he wrote in reply, explaining that greediness and avidity for land is in reality only the means to enable us to perform our accustomed acts of hospitality. For my part, I have taken Brother Anselm as my mentor.

Every day he sits in the Scriptorium section of the library, copying a chapter of St. Mark's Gospel on to parchment. Will he ever finish it?

It's my job to wash the tiled floor of the library whilst the choir monks are in Chapel. One day there was a monk in the library. I wondered why he wasn't in Chapel with the others. Imagine my surprise, when he lifted 'his' hood to reveal the long hair of a woman.

'What are you doing here?' I gasped.

'I am here so that my soul may enter the gate of heaven,' she whispered fervently.

The rules of the Order I knew did not allow such things; the rings on her fingers told of her wealth and no doubt she had given generously, but it was for God to judge the abbot—not I. So I continued my labours. I like working there for the library is next to the calefactory or warming room with its comforting fireplace. Monks love to cluster round it, as this is the only room in which we are allowed to warm ourselves.

Even if my poor legs are numb with cold, my heart is always warmed by the sight of Brother Anselm's quill pens on his desk next to his pots of black and coloured inks. He spends days sometimes on an illuminated letter, the first letter of the first word on the page, exquisitely drawn and decorated in the brightest colours.

The initial has little people perched on its extremities, captured in magic circles which intertwine with others. Within this orderly maze, he paints the flowers and herbs he sees round the abbey— vetch, cowslip, shepherd's purse. 'Flowers and herbs will teach you a lesson you never heard from masters in school', he says. His favourite is the rose-petalled willow-herb or fireweed which sets alight the slopes of our orchards, 'like the flames of Pentecost', according to Brother Anselm.

One day, I cease my scrubbing to read aloud (for I can read, thanks to Brother Joseph) the text that lies open on Brother Anselm's desk. Unbeknown to me, the abbot is standing in an alcove listening. I fall to my knees in penance; my legs give way and I collapse in an undignified heap before him.

'How long hast thou been with us as a lay brother, Brother Edgar?' he asks as he helps me to my feet.

'Five years this Michaelmas, my lord,' I reply, wondering what is coming next.

'And how much of that time hast thou spent in the scriptorium?' I fear a reprimand for indeed I deserve it.

Instead I learn that if I study hard, I can spend the next year preparing to be a choir monk under the supervision of the Master of the Novices. So follows my noviciate, a full, exacting twelve months.

I can't believe it when I find myself walking along the newly built ambulatory with the other choir monks and saying all seven offices of the day. At last I can give myself to the study of the scriptures and reach mystical union with God.

Dear Brother Joseph shares my joy, but alas the bell which calls me seven times a day to worship now imposes too great a burden on him. One memorable morning, he falls at Prime and is carried out by two of the monks back to the pallet bed in his own infirmary. Before the service has ended, he is dead. How bitterly I reproach God for my twisted legs. Had it not been for them, I could have borne him to his bed and been there to share his Last Sacrament.

I fear I have betrayed my dear old friend, without whose guidance I could never have been a choir monk.

The good Abbot Henricus sits against the east wall of the chapter house and listens to my confession. 'Brother Joseph saw thee last saying thy office in Chapel', he grunts consolingly, 'no greater comfort could'st thou have given him.'

I know he is right and I thank God. Never again must I reproach the Almighty for my deformity.

The years pass. The building work continues. Then suddenly, the abbot believing his own days to be numbered, announces that the abbey is almost complete. It must be consecrated, for in the early stages it had only been blessed.

Alas that such a holy enterprise should provoke dispute and possible bloodshed. Our abbey is in the parish of Bacton in the diocese of Hereford. It's therefore right that Bishop Cantilupe of Hereford should consecrate it. Yet we all know our abbey has frequently been described as being in Wales. Indeed we are anxious to be classed among the Welsh abbeys for taxation purposes to avoid heavier payment. 'You can't have your cake and eat it too,' declares the bishop of St. David's, who claims that Dore Abbey is in the parish of Ewyas Harold and therefore in 'his' diocese. Unfortunately he then buys the support of the treacherous Baron Tregoz, the nephew of Thomas Cantilupe, who thinks nothing of betraying his uncle. A nasty piece of work is this baron and not above murdering an uncle for personal gain.

Imagine our horror on the day of the consecration to see the baron's men camped on the river bank opposite the abbey. The lay brothers are instructed by the abbot to meet Bishop Cantilupe and conduct him safely to the abbey gatehouse. We choir monks are to pray for his safety. The waiting is unbearable. We comfort ourselves with gossip—more like fishwives than monks: he is known to be a strong, stern man and sterner on himself than on any other; he wears a hair shirt for his own self-discipline and mortification. Such spirit cannot be deterred by a mere show of military force. Hasn't he publicly whipped Lord Clifford before the cathedral's high altar for ill-treating his tenants?

Meanwhile, the lay brothers are witnessing a terrible scene. Baron Tregoz gallops across the river with a posse of armed men. 'Go back to your own diocese, uncle,' he shouts. 'If you reach Dore today, you'll not leave it alive!'

The bishop reigns in his horse and signs to his escort to withdraw from his person. Reluctantly they obey, leaving him to face his turbulent nephew. 'I am come to consecrate Dore Abbey,' he announces with dignity. 'He who dares prevent me is answerable to God!'

Baron Tregoz's hand rests on his sword as though it's paralysed. The brothers told us afterwards that he seemed unable to move or speak until the bishop had passed on his way.

And so Bishop Cantilupe arrives, punctually, to perform the consecration of Dore Abbey.

How can I ever forget my first sight of him? He's extraordinary. No mitre can hide his red hair. His nose is so large—it's almost a joke, but not quite, for there's a strange aura of spirituality about him which makes my flesh tingle.

The consecration passes without incident. The farewells are said, the bishop and his entourage leave the abbey for the gatehouse. Then I hear, as in a dream, the voice of Brother Joseph bidding me follow the bishop.

I do. Why have I reached the gatehouse without falling? I'm no longer hobbling. I'm walking straight—on straight legs! Praise God! My prayer has been answered!

Blanche Parry of Bacton

am old and my sight is failing. I strain my eyes—if only I could finish the embroidery on my court dress. The white corded silk is shot with silver, powdered with bunches of flowers. They are flowers from my home in Bacton, so far away on the borders of Wales. It's many years since I was there. I wonder, do the daffodils still bloom in the Spring on the hill behind our house? Amongst the daffodils my needle has woven roses and honeysuckle that climbed up the walls of our manor house at New Court.

I can see them now ... and there is my carriage bumping up the long track that cuts through the fields of our estate. On the left the hill rises gently, the few trees on its green scalp erupting from the castle ruins to be combed by the wind. On the right, only feet away, is the River Dore, or the River of Gold as we children used to call it. I can hear the rushing water but I can't see it because of the alders that cling to the bank like sentries. The heavy scent of white hawthorn drugs my senses.

Tears blur my failing vision as I struggle with a French knot. But my mistress mustn't see my tears. Who will believe that the queen's chief gentlewoman, known for her crabbed austerity, is given to tears? 'Only Blanche Parry,' they whisper, 'dares to admonish Her Majesty!' It's true enough for Elizabeth has met with my thin-lipped disapproval on many occasions. I know her better than she knows herself and she knows me better than anyone else. That is why she mustn't see my tears: mustn't know how much I wish to leave the Court ... to die at home.

I must concentrate on gold acorns created by man not God. Gold acorns and oak leaves adorned one of the queen's gowns until she lost them at Westminster last May. Typical! That girl has a curious inability to keep her gold accessories attached to her person! She confessed her carelessness to me with a humility unseen by others. How can I ever leave her? She is my life, I have served her for over fifty years.

Little Elizabeth was only three when I was given full charge of her. Poor babe, I rocked her cradle and comforted her when her luckless mother, Anne Boleyn, was executed.

The child was like a daughter to me: more than a daughter for she was my sovereign too. I remained a maid in Court and was no man's wife. Now in my old age I am content to know that I have shared the celibacy of my beloved queen.

She was such a pretty little girl, so hard to control in the demanding years of her adolescence. How right I was to speak my mind to that swine of a Lord High Admiral, Thomas Seymour, when he trifled with the affections of my princess.

'Be about your business, Mistress Parry,' the saucy rogue ordered as he strode into her bedchamber, bare-legged in his night-gown and slippers, and tickled my Lady Elizabeth in her bed.

'And be about yours, my lord,' I retorted. Just because he had married the late king's queen he thought he could have her step daughter too.

I alone knew she lost her virginity to that scoundrel. She was just fourteen. I personally scrubbed the fur rug that lay on her four-

poster that night so no-one else would see the blood. Thereafter her menstruations were irregular. That incident affected her health and left its mark on her precocious and impressionable mind.

They were dangerous times alright. The Duke of Somerset was ruling on behalf of her sickly young half-brother, Edward. Plots were rife. I knelt behind my lady when she asked the duke for his protection. Thank God he was touched by her innocence and executed the dastardly Seymour! The axe ended his secret schemes to marry my lady.

Her Majesty calls me. I hear her voice but her face is blurred. The onslaught of blindness has its compensations for now her quest for perpetual youth is fulfilled in my memory. I blame myself now for feeding her vanity. Why, oh why did I let my young Welsh cousin John Dee bewitch her?

Was I not bewitched myself by his beauty? His long beard was as white as milk. He wore a long gown that rustled as he walked and did not kneel but boldly stood before her and prophesied 'Thou art the rightful sovereign of strange and far-distant thrones. The very stars combine in their courses to flatter thy Divine Majesty.'

I remember the day my mistress and I visited him at his home in Mortlake. There he stood beneath the churchyard wall, persuading her to look into his magic mirror. Alas no wizard, however charming, could give her eternal youth. She could not bear to see her own beauty fade. Yet she never minced words concerning the attractions of others.

'Dear Blanche,' she would say, 'how can'st thou understand? Thy face is plain. Neither ha'st thou ever made the best of thyself! Thy plain and unfashionable gown with those long hanging sleeves puts me quite out of countenance. Thou art still wearing that flat cap with a veil, long since gone out of fashion.'

She only pretends to object to my simple tastes for she actually delights in them. The chief gentlewoman in her simple dress provides a fitting contrast to the glittering queen with her heavy jewelled chain and farthingale starred with gems. I am no lover of ornament but the queen craves finery of every description. She even demands regular tokens of loyalty from her servants, especially on New Year's Day. My last gift to her was an armband embroidered with tiny pearls and garnished with gold.

Of course she is very generous in return. She has provided me with my own special coach and horses with grooms. Thus I travel in comfort when I accompany her on royal tours throughout the country. What progresses those were! Cooks, butlers, stable boys, scullions and even the sempstress whose job consisted only of sewing pearls on the queen's dress. It is well such progresses are mostly confined to the south of the country for my folk on the Welsh borders could never bear the expense, nor believe their eyes. Imagine four hundred carts carrying piles of clothes and linen, tableware, documents and furnishings—plus the coverings for the queen's bed and numerous valuables from which she will not be parted.

As keeper of the queen's jewels (for which I am paid the princely sum of £33. 6s. 8d. a year), I have to keep an account of the many gifts she receives.

Her Majesty's extravagance extends to those near and dear. Her generosity enabled me to buy the patronage of tithes of Sutton St. Michael and the Chapel of Wisteston. She has granted me the manor of Fawley, the fishing in the Wye, a water mill and meadows in Marden and rents in Wellington. Those gifts were made with a smile, 'We know thou would'st rather have lands in thy beloved Herefordshire than rings on thy fingers, Blanche!'

She also knows I yearn to return, but my needs must submit to hers. I pour oil on her troubled waters, easing the tensions caused by Lord Burghley. Who else is there to comfort her? Who else is there to listen? Above all, who else can be trusted to keep her secrets? Behind the doors of the queen's private chambers, with the curtains drawn, I have listened patiently to her ragings against courtiers who have displeased her. Who else knows about her involvement in the murder of the Earl of Leicester's wife? The queen's brittle love affair with the earl was common knowledge, not so the dark intrigue surrounding his wife's murder. That was confined to the royal bedchamber.

It hasn't all been comfort and support. My mistress is not so proud that she can't learn. I have taught her Welsh—she has a feeling for the language of her ancestors.

'My forefathers came from Wales too, Blanche,' she declares. 'Tell us about thy home on the borders.'

So I tell her. When I was a girl, I would hitch up my petticoats to climb the hill behind New Court to the remains of Bacton Castle. My father disapproved but mother was one of thirteen children and had also behaved in an unladylike manner in her youth.

I liked to climb up the path to the top of the motte. They say William de Bacton built the castle about three hundred years ago. Father told me, however, that there was once an earlier castle on that site, built by the Normans to defend the Marches against the Welsh. It was hard to imagine it for there was only earth where once were walls. Only the shepherd lived up there now in a cottage built, perhaps, from material scavenged from the castle.

It was very windy at that height. I'd stand on the mound of what was once the bailey and look down on the thatched roof of our house. Beyond were hawthorn bushes, whiter than the ground alabaster I apply to my mistress's skin. Across the valley snaked the green alders from which our cobbler made clogs. They marked the path of the secret river, buried like gold from my sight.

No pails of muck and urine emptied into the London streets, no need of scent to disguise unpleasant smells, the air was so fresh up there. Sometimes I yearn for solitude like that, with only the sheep for company: the plaintive cries, lost in the wind, of new born lambs looking for browsing ewes.

At Christmas time we would gather the holly from bushes that seem to have sprouted like magic from the brookside. In the Spring bird's eye, clover, buttercups and daisies would likewise thrust their way through the rocks and wind-swept grass. But it was a castle once up there on Bacton Hill, the red of its exposed rocks like scabs of old wounds.

There was that Sunday when I scrambled up the hill in my best gown and my scarlet shoes, I was ready for church early. Rumour had it that the Pope was sending a part of the 'true cross' to our border counties. My sisters were excited and argued whether it would come to St. Faith's in Bacton. Would we see it? Touch it? I dare not tell them I didn't care. For me, the view from the top of the hill was more precious, more divine than superstitious relics.

'Mistress Blanche,' my governess greeted me crossly on seeing my mud-stained gown and shoes, 'you will never make a gentlewoman!'

I was determined to prove her wrong as I hastily changed into my
second best gown and my russet shoes. We had to use the carriage
for church for St. Faith's was in the southern part of the parish and
some distance from the house. Familiar open fields and apple
orchards rippled past our carriage windows, giving us time to
compose ourselves for Sunday worship.

The church, built like New Court on the side of a hill, was some
three hundred years old when I was a girl. It had recently been
rebuilt and lengthened. Above its moulded wallplates were small
carved angels which reminded me of the butterflies on my hill.

I prayed for King Harry and Cardinal Wolsey and drank the
Blessed Blood of Our Lord Jesus Christ from the Bacton Cup. It's a
beautiful silver chalice with curious leopard masks round its base. It

has the name 'John Capull' engraved on it. Father told me there was a mayor of Gloucester called Capull in 1484 who gave this chalice to the Fraternity of New Llanthony at Gloucester. Priests from that order often celebrated Mass for us at St. Faith's which is how we believe the Bacton Cup came to the church.

My royal mistress, when she was Princess Elizabeth, would ask me to tell her the story of St. Faith ... again and again. It helped to reconcile her to the cruel death of her mother for St. Faith was also beheaded, though after suffering torture on a grid-iron. Her emblems are therefore a sword and a grid-iron. The young princess would wince when I told of the execution but insisted on my finishing the tale. 'Spare me no detail, Mistress Blanche,' she would say, 'I need the heart and stomach of a king and the courage of St. Faith to rule my kingdom.'

It all seems so long ago. I can no longer see to finish the embroidery on my court dress. I shall never wear it now, indeed I have a strange desire to see it spread over the altar in Bacton Church.

I day dream, or have I the gift of prophecy? Do I see Bacton Church three hundred years hence? A stone wall and wooden kissing gate separate it from gnarled apple trees in the long grass. Wild parsley swamps a rusty barn to the right of the church. There are no human voices, but the wind speaks in the grass; a cuckoo declares itself in the woods beyond and the church clock chimes the hour. Countryside and church are one.

Inside, the church is very dark. Are those oil-lamps? Is that the Last Supper carved over the altar? What is this fine monument in cold marble? There's something eerily familiar about the figure kneeling in her full gown with tight-fitting bodice, sleeves with ruffs round the wrists and a scent box in her right hand. The other is the queen ... Gloriana on her throne ... Is she calling me?

I can't see the anxious face peering through the silk hangings of my bed, but I know it's not the queen. A maid-in-waiting announces that the physician has arrived to bleed me.

'Send for Lord Burghley,' I gasp. He must supervise my will. He will see it performed according to my desire, for charity's sake.

So shall I die, peacefully, knowing I have left £500 for an alms-house in Bacton where the oldest and poorest shall find relief, whether they be men or women. The highway between New Court and Hampton shall be repaired at my expense.

To the queen, my sovereign lady and mistress, I give my best diamond (and I pray she'll not lose it!)

At the Court I have lived my life. It's fitting that my body will lie near my queen, at St. Margaret's in the City of Westminster. Yet the seat of my feelings and humours lies in my bowels. Therefore my bowels must go to Bacton, for Bacton is my home, my childhood heaven.

Alice Foster of Brockhampton

ee Mama, I'm so glad you're happy about it!'

I was surprised at her whole-hearted acceptance of my fiancé. He was not one of the wealthy eligible Americans who dined with us regularly at home in Massachusetts. Indeed no. He was the second son of a Yorkshire mill owner with no prospect of inheriting the family fortune—and with a love of raucous brass bands to boot. Not that I had known any of this when I first met him on a cruise beneath a bright tropical moon.

Yet Arthur Wellesley Foster, with his deep Yorkshire accent awkwardly disguised by his Oxford education, was the answer to my prayer, even when I saw him in the more realistic setting of his home in Black Dyke Mills.

'Sure he loves you, honey?' from Papa meant 'Did he love my money?'

Astonishingly, Mama rose to Arthur's defence. 'Have you no soul, Ebenezer?' she demanded. 'Here's Alice about to marry into the English aristocracy, no doubt taking tea with her majesty before the year's out, and here you are questioning the young man's intentions—shame on you!'

Of course, Mama had the wrong idea, but I wasn't going to disillusion her. Arthur didn't move in court circles. In fact he had followed the usual avenue for second sons and gone into the church, but Mama was not to be outdone: her Alice was going to be Lady of the Manor and no mistake—and that's how Arthur and I came to live at Brockhampton Court, near Ross-on-Wye.

Brockhampton was a very large country mansion surrounded by extensive lawns and six acres of parkland. Mama spotted it when we were touring through the beautiful Wye Valley in early spring, on our way to Wales.

'This could be the place for you, Alice!' she said, and promptly instructed our coachman to drive us down the long private drive. The driveway followed the line of a seemingly private green valley inhabited only by a few sheep, to eventually melt into dipping parkland before the mansion. I glanced at Arthur, but he was silent. He had quickly learnt from Papa that resistance to Mama was futile. Englishmen tended to find her overpowering; they weren't used to modern American women like us.

The owner of Brockhampton Court, Sir Robert Lighton, was a case in point. No sooner had the coachman opened the carriage door for mama to alight than he appeared on horseback to pay his respects. He was fairly young, still in his thirties, but he had been responsible for building the spacious mansion which stood on the site of an earlier house, Upper Court, the ancestral home of the Skyrme family. Despite our unexpected arrival he greeted us with formal courtesy, acknowledging Mama's raptures over his property with an invitation to tea.

We were ushered into the Great Hall by the butler who took our cloaks, muffs and woollen gloves, while we warmed ourselves by the fire that roared in the deep stone fireplace. Sir Robert joined us, to be promptly followed by a footman who served us tea from a trolley with two shelves laden with sandwiches and delicious pastries.

Mama made her bid for his estate before the poor man had sampled one of his own sandwiches. Stunned by her generous offer and needing time to gather his thoughts, he mentioned he was born on American Independence Day. Mama hailed it as an omen and the deal was soon clinched.

'Brockhampton Court is our wedding present to you, Alice darling, and to you too of course, dear Arthur. May you both be very happy there.'

Arthur fought with embarrassment and embarrassment lost. He wasn't one to look a gift horse in the face. Anyway, as I was always telling him: they could afford it; they owned the largest department store in New England: Jordan, March and Co. 'And we'll find a way to repay them, Arthur. I'm my mother's daughter, you know.'

We moved into Brockhampton in 1894—after Papa had made some alterations, with Mama's help. She wanted it in Elizabethan style, 'More historic' she said. 'No-one will know it's pseudo.' So that's why Brockhampton Court is unique—an Elizabethan styled nineteenth century mansion.

We then turned our attention to the scattered cottages outside our private grounds where lived those in service at the Court. Their simple homes were in urgent need of repair. Most had only one room downstairs, but folk made the best of it. There were geraniums and sweet smelling musk on the window-sills. On one occasion a sudden call of nature forced me to use one of their privies and I was amazed to find the wooden seat scrubbed white and the brick floor raddled.

We also had to build more cottages to accommodate extra staff. Arthur had a habit of appointing anyone who could either play the trumpet or cricket! 'Did he come recommended?' I asked on meeting our new under-gardener, only to be told that he was a good bowler.

We needed the under-gardener anyway. We had a large walled kitchen garden, a veritable sun-trap and shelter for our more sensitive plants. Broad beans as big as halfpennies and rotund sweet green peas were among the fresh vegetables served daily in our oak-panelled dining-room. Gentry for miles around would also come to admire my rare Brockhampton daffodil with a brilliant orange frill in its centre.

Oh yes, in my new role as Lady of the Manor, my popularity was assured. The old adage that you have to be born in Herefordshire to be accepted is nonsense. Throughout the county I quickly became known as the most generous benefactress, whose donations to hospitals and special appeals were gratefully received: Herefordshire had taken me to its heart.

As for Arthur, he became 'the Colonel' to the locals. It wasn't fitting to use 'the Reverend' now that we had appointed the Reverend Nott as our incumbent. As befitted the landowner of a country seat, Arthur became involved in local government instead. In addition to being a J.P. and Deputy Lieutenant of the county, he was also made High Sheriff.

Although we were both so busy in the county, our happiest times were spent at home. Arthur was a keen sportsman and an excellent shot. Our gamekeeper bred the pheasants and organised the shoots on our estate.

'Why does father shoot the pretty birds?' our small son, Cuthbert, wanted to know one day. We were watching some cock pheasants emerge from our wood with their scarlet-circled eyes and iridescent sheen of green and purple illuminating their chestnut-brown plumage.

'Don't fret little master,' chuckled our gamekeeper, 'pheasants are daft birds, they don't know what's going on. Do you know I put down a bucket with barely six inches of water in it, yet when I came back a few minutes later, four baby pheasants had drowned themselves. What's more, at the beginning of the season they haven't even learnt to fly away from the guns.'

After the shoot, the beaters would sit down to soup, bread, cheese and homemade pickles in our kitchen while braces were hung on hooks in the larder. When the time came for them to be roasted, cook served them with roast potatoes, brussel sprouts, red currant jelly and her speciality: gooseberry jam to bring out the flavour.

Salmon fishing was another of Arthur's favourite pastimes; again we dined off the result. Brockhampton estate includes some of the finest fishing on the Wye.

There's an amazing view of the curving river from the prehistoric Capler Camp. They say Caractacus used the summit of the hill to build his camp when he retreated from Little Doward to

21

Herefordshire Beacon. From the summit our woodland drops sharply down to the river far below. It amazed me how the trees stayed upright on the steep descent as I watched Nanny climb or rather, slide down after my two sons from lofty Capler to the banks of the Wye.

In winter, ice and snow made the steep road from Capler Hill to the next village of Fownhope impassable. There was little traffic anyway, apart from our carriage and the occasional wagon or farmer on horseback. We were content, Arthur and I, for be it winter or summer, Brockhampton was a beautiful place—and we owned it. Capler Hill was the centre of our world.

It took me about half an hour to walk home from the hill, down the winding country lane to where the lodge stood at the gates. Once in the park, I would make straight for my summer house. There a footman, anticipating my arrival, waited to serve tea. I could then gaze at the immaculate lawns and shaped hedges and decide that the new under-gardener was earning his keep.

There was never much time to stand and stare—not with the next party always to organize. That stone Chinese lantern in the garden had given my parties a new dimension: it was very popular with the young gentlemen, for it gave them an excuse to take their young ladies for a walk in the garden.

I suppose I never quite became used to having a church in my garden. It was on the opposite side of the manor to my summer house. I could even see its tiny bell tower from my bedroom window. In Massachusetts the churches were on separate sites in the middle of towns.

Ironically, it was the sense of history that made me uneasy in church. Sitting in the front pew, I was aware that others had once sat there. It wasn't my church, it was theirs. It was a very small church, only forty feet long but everywhere there were reminders of former owners of the Court. Names like William Stallard and the Reverend Sir Robert Lighton stared at me constantly from the walls. They weren't my ancestors, simply my predecessors and there's the rub!

Mama didn't help. 'Think of all the people who've been baptised in this, Alice,' she constantly breathed over the eight hundred year old font.

As for Papa, he enjoyed just listening to the organ. 'No finer memorial than a church, honey,' was his favourite comment. I was never to forget those words.

Oh yes, I thought Holy Trinity's a memorial alright, but to whom? I knew only the names of those commemorated inside, while the little churchyard surreptitiously hid the past from me as though I were some ignorant intruder. If only that ancient yew would tell me its story. Who had hidden in its trunk? It was wide

enough to shelter seven men. I felt the presence of those who once had knelt before the fourteenth century churchyard cross, but their identity was a mystery.

My parents' deaths decided me: I would build a new church, it would be their memorial. 'No finer memorial than a church, Papa,' I murmured to myself as I came to terms with my grief. My church would be unique. Ebenezer and Julia Jordan deserved the best and the best they should have.

'I want a church that's both modern and medieval,' I told Arthur. 'Impossible!' He replied. But that was before he'd heard of W.R. Lethaby. Lethaby was the famous Arts and Crafts architect and a follower of William Morris. My friend Alexandra, who was a patron of fine art in Birmingham, recommended him, for his reputation was second to none.

I promptly sent him a message to come and see me at once. He ignored it. Alexandra explained. 'Lethaby dislikes being ordered about by the rich. He'll only respond to a polite request.'

I submitted and he came. 'Before I undertake this commission, Mrs. Foster,' he said, 'it's quite important that we understand each other. My ideal of beauty is a brown bread and dewy morning, not a champagne supper. The spiritual qualities in architecture place it above mere building.'

I knew I had met my match. All that mattered was that he accepted the commission. No-one else could do Mama and Papa justice.

'I leave it entirely to you,' I replied, 'provided you give me the best of everything and spare no expense.'

He agreed, for here was his chance to put into practice his own theories of design without financial constraint. And so All Saints, the church with a thatched roof, was built. It was to stand across the road from the west gate of our estate, conveniently accessible for us and yet outside our private parkland. It never occurred to me that it would therefore be isolated from any village community that it might have served.

Lethaby himself was so committed to it that he made frequent journeys from London to supervise the work. Consequently he nearly had a nervous breakdown through the frustration of wasting time on the steam train to Hereford and then waiting for the carriage to pick him up at the station for the ten mile drive to Brockhampton.

Nevertheless, the foundation stone was laid on 25 June, 1901. Only sixteen months later the bishop of Hereford consecrated All Saints, in October, 1902. Thereafter services ceased to be held in Holy Trinity. Gradually nature claimed it; now it's just an ivy-clad ruin in my garden, roofless, forlorn and hidden by trees.

All Saints, however, has become an artist's paradise. One of the most beautiful and peaceful valleys in the world now contains Lethaby's masterpiece. The church's roof thatched with Norfolk reed complements the buff stone tower and walls, softened by creepers and flowering trees.

The view from the church door of the gentle valley dotted with sheep and ridged with trees is rarely disturbed by tourists, even in high Summer. Summer has even entered the church. All the wild flowers of Herefordshire are carved on the forty-eight panels of the choir stalls. Clinging to the font is a delicate trailing grapevine— made of stone! Country folk are also captured by the sculptor, for they can be seen on the pulpit, listening to Christ's teaching while their children play.

Of course Lethaby employed the best artists and craftsmen. The tapestries were made in the William Morris workshop from designs by Burne-Jones. The stained glass was made in the famous Christopher Wall studios. How I love the south window, a special memorial to Papa. It pictures an angel choir 'for music ever found an echo in his heart.'

The west window is dedicated to Lethaby's own father. That's what comes of giving your architect complete freedom! Still, it is a beautiful window featuring St. Cecilia, the patron saint of music, with a cat and kitten at her feet.

There will come a time, I know, when I enter All Saints for the last time. It does not distress me, for I am at peace here.

Rosamund Clifford of Clifford

Hergest, why are your songs so sad? I see my reflection in your soulful eyes. You sing of my beauty, turning a reason for joy into sorrow. Your fingers ripple over your harp strings and the music flows effortlessly like the river that winds round my father's castle, my home, at Clifford.

Hergest remembers when I was born. It was just after his father was killed in battle when he was only five. Now he is eighteen and he is still sad. His blonde hair falls across his face as he sings. His attire seems outlandish for he wears a crude monk-like robe with wide sleeves lined in buttercup yellow. Round his waist is the scarlet girdle I bought for him at the fair, as a Christmas present several years ago.

'I have a song for thee, Lady Jane, if thou would'st hear it.'

Perhaps he will sing of my forthcoming marriage? For I'm thirteen and soon Father will be wanting to arrange an alliance for me, as he has done for my older sisters.

But what is this song? Hergest sings of a rose so perfect that the sun is dazzled by its perfection. A fair lady sees the rose opening its petals to the sun and becomes jealous. Her eyes glitter strangely and shrink in her head until they become serpent's eyes—the fair lady is transformed into a fierce dragon whose sulphurous breath instantly destroys the rose. The sun mourns the loss and darkness floods the world at the song's end.

I shudder at the thought of the lady's serpent eyes. I will not be tormented by my father's minstrel. I need to escape: to climb to the top of the keep: to feel alive and powerful—and why not? Surely Clifford Castle is the most commanding place on earth? It was built by William FitzOsborn 150 feet above the crossing on the River Wye. My father says it's an important castle because it's the most westerly stronghold and holds the key to the Upper Wye Valley.

We Cliffords are proud of our Norman ancestry, proud to own one of the five great castles which the brave FitzOsborn built. We're proud too, of our Saxon connections. My grandfather took the local name of Clifford when he married Margaret, daughter and heiress of Ralph de Thony of Clifford Castle.

'Clifford isn't like other Norman castles, Jane,' my father tells me, 'for we have dug a ditch above the steep cliff and made a hall and shell keep for our burgesses.'

These are dangerous times we live in, with England in the grip of a civil war till Matilda can win the crown from that weakling, Stephen. Meanwhile, over the border in Wales live the terrible Owain Gwynedd and Rhys ap Gruffyd, whose attacks our castles are built to withstand. That's why our castle includes protection for the villagers. Their living accommodation is virtually contained within the inner side of our curtain wall, where there's an extra hall and little keep. Sixteen men live there with their families and there's room too for the pigs, goats and sheep. The place is a mass of granaries, store-houses, baking and brewing sheds fitted in amongst the stables and barracks.

'I know our castle is different, sir,' I assure my father, 'for isn't Clifford Castle on top of the world?'

He laughs, 'Thou art right, my little princess! Never settle for anything less!'

Let him laugh. I can see the whole world from the keep. The Black Mountains rear up from Wales on the one side and the cliff drops away to meet the Wye on the other. I'm the centre of a vast magic circle. It must be magic, for I know the world is square. An audacious breeze lifts my long hair which is tightly plaited to my waist. I ignore it, though the wind gathers. I am in charge of the world. I am queen of the castle. Father has often said in jest that I will control kings.

A gusty wind suddenly penetrates my heavy cloak. Pressing against the inner wall of the keep in order to control my swirling cloak, I look over the top at the snake-like ivy creeping up the walls. I shudder and glance towards the Black Mountains for reassurance, just as the Devil himself draws his grey curtains over Hay Bluff. He has blotted out my world. I can barely make out my father's men-at-arms riding across the drawbridge. I listen for the familiar sound of their horses' hooves on the bridge timbers but I can only hear the howling gale.

Lightning blinks brightly; rain slashes my face. One of the guards shouts at me above the exploding thunder, ''Tis too stormy my lady, pray seek the shelter of the hall.'

Even down in the hall it's impossible to keep out the wind. Shutters drawn across window-holes rattle in the gusts. Smoke billows down the vent, while the fire spits and sizzles at the intruding rain.

The household has already gathered for supper. A squire brings me a cup of wine while I recline on the dais at the end of the hall. The torches flare brightly in their iron-holders round the walls.

Hergest has put his harp away in its bag of embroidered leather for tonight we are entertained by a travelling acrobat. He brings tidings of Queen Matilda's son, Prince Henry, who, it is rumoured, will end this terrible civil war.

My father raises his goblet and announces that Christ and His Saints have woken at last, for they must surely have slept through these days of terrible plunder and slaughter. God could not have known of the cruel tortures going on in every castle dungeon in the kingdom.

I may only be thirteen but I know my father's face glows in the amber light. He is numbered amongst Prince Henry's loyal barons. Woe betide the rebellious barons of the Marches for Prince Henry is even now on his way to deal with them, my father continues, confirming the acrobat's news. He will be staying briefly at Clifford.

'What is Prince Henry like?' I ask Hergest, for minstrels being borrowed by neighbouring barons hear much gossip.

Hergest frowns. 'Like a coin, my lady, the Prince hath two sides. He is hard but he is just; generous but demanding; friendly but shrewd.'

Still he has not told me what I want to know. 'Has he a wife?'

'Indeed he hath, my lady. He wed Eleanor of Aquitaine last summer. Thereby hangs a tale not fit for a gentle lady's ears.'

I wheedle it out of Hergest by degrees. Eleanor was old and secondhand. I feel really sorry for Prince Henry. She had previously been married to the French king, Louis VII, for fourteen years— longer than I had actually lived! Unfortunately, Louis found her too lively, while she said it was more like being married to a monk than a king. They visited the Pope who actually forced them to sleep in the same bed! Shortly afterwards, Eleanor was shocked to find she was bearing a child, for her contempt for her husband's love-making was well known. She gave birth to a daughter, not the longed-for son, and that finished the marriage. The French have a way of getting out of these things—Louis and Eleanor were declared to be too closely related, so the marriage was dissolved. Louis lost Aquitaine, some half of his kingdom, and our Prince Henry, heir to the English throne, snapped it up by marrying Eleanor.

Theirs was a marriage of convenience, of course. Nevertheless, I wish she had had that son and remained Queen of France.

Clifford Castle was soon throbbing in anticipation of the visit. I personally shake the fleas and dust from the best sheepskin rug for his bed. The walls ring with the clash of the armourers' hammers as war gear is forged and mended. But his coming is an anti-climax. The lavish feast prepared in his honour does not interest him. He tosses his half-chewed chunk of roast pig to the dogs and rises to discuss strategy with my father, who signs for the feast to be cleared away. Many haven't finished eating, but the rushes are immediately laid out and the sleeping bench against the wall made up with the best sheepskin rug and hard straw-filled pillows for the prince.

'No time for sleep!' is the royal retort.

'You must rest my lord!' cries a soft, sweet voice. Did I really say that? My concern had made me forget my manners.

There was an embarrassed hush as he turns and notices me for the first time. Fearfully, I return his gaze.

He isn't handsome, nor is he tall. Indeed he is a trifle corpulent for a youth of twenty. But he is strong—his whole body spells strength: his stout figure, his bullneck, his broad shoulders and his powerful arms—and England needs a strong king.

'Forgive my daughter's impertinence, sire,' my father is saying. I bow my head in humiliation and sink into a low curtsy.

The prince moves towards me. I feel his hand lift my chin. I gaze into his freckled face. If only I could reach out and touch his closely cropped red hair. His keen grey eyes search my face. Then he is kissing my hand and whispering, 'Save thyself for the king, O Rosa Mundi.'

I am so overcome, I cannot reply. His hand is still holding mine when he turns to my father with, 'You have the Rose of the World for a daughter, Baron Walter.'

I have undergone a royal baptism: I am no longer Jane, I am Rosamund.

In the morning he has gone. The state documents were hastily reloaded on to the pack horses during the night so that Prince Henry might leave at dawn for the next castle, the next loyal baron.

I am bereft, abandoned. My prince has ridden into the sun. I am asleep and do not see him go. My fevered imagination compensates: I see his short red hair haloed in sunlight. I forget he already has a queen. I am a virgin, just thirteen. I am his Rose of the World. I dwell on his few precious words. I am his forever.

I share my feelings with no-one, not even Hergest—least of all Hergest.

I'll never forget this day, the day my prince left Clifford. The storms have passed. It is one of those cloudy summer days typical of the Marches. As my father, with a retinue of men-at-arms is abroad, escorting the prince to Ewyas Harold, I tell the guard at the gatehouse that I have his leave to visit the Cluniac monks at the priory. I am embroidering a cope, I tell him; I need advice on the design.

My needlework is much admired at the castle, indeed I am rather conceited about it myself. When I finish that cope I will embroider my name upon it. It shall read: Rosamund Clifford made me with her own hands.

I don't go down Succour Lane to the priory, however, but take my own path down to the River Wye. It is steep and muddy from the rain. I use one of the many branches brought down in the storm as a walking stick, beating down the nettles and giant parsley. Then I am grabbing at the ivy and strangling columbine with one hand and digging my stick into the mud to steady myself with the other. So I slip and slide down to the river.

I see my face in the moving water. It distorts my features. What if he is disappointed when he sees me again? The river refuses to reassure me. It carries my future round its shingly bend to some unknown destination. Only the swans, white dots in the distance, know what lies round that bend. If the river could speak it would tell me that two years would pass before I hear from my prince.

His coronation comes and goes. He has crushed the power of the unruly barons and all men obey the king and his law.

In the early summer of my fifteenth year, I receive an invitation from the nuns who have a house at Middeley provided by the father of three of the nuns who said they were too confined at Godstow, their spiritual home. It's a pleasant place by a river.

As soon as I arrive I notice how excited the nuns are. 'The king is here,' they giggle. 'He awaits you in the garden.'

I catch my breath. I cannot believe it. At last he has sent for me.

He is taller, stronger even than I remember. He holds a pink and white rose in his hand. 'For you,' he murmurs, 'my knights brought it back from the Holy Land. I have named it Rosa Mundi—after you, my Rose of the World.'

When I return to Clifford I see the castle from afar, crowning the rugged face of precipitous rock that sweeps down to the Wye. I too am proud and momentarily invincible. I care not that the world knows I am no longer a virgin. I want to shout from the keep 'the king has taken my maidenhood.' My strong king will give me a strong son; I shall call him William.

Hergest's harp interrupts my thoughts. He is trying out a new song in the hall. No-one listens. The women are busy feathering fowls, the scullion turning a pig on the spit. The familiar smoky atmosphere enfolds me. Poor Hergest, I at least will listen to his song.

At first I think dear Hergest is celebrating my union with the king, but I am quickly disillusioned.

> Beloved of a king,
> Of Rosamund I sing.
>
> O, Jealousy is ever green,
> Beware the vengeance
> Of his queen.
>
> A labyrinth the king chose
> In tender caution for dear Rose,
> As Eleanor's anger daily grows.
>
> O, Jealousy is ever green,
> Beware the vengeance
> Of his queen.
>
> Only Henry held the key
> To the maze's secrecy;
> Safe she'd be, but never free.
>
> O, Jealousy is ever green,
> Beware the vengeance
> Of his queen.
>
> But on his foot was a thread,
> To his love, the Queen it led
> Filling Rosamund with dread.

O, Jealousy is ever green,
Beware the vengeance
Of his queen.

No escape, she had to choose:
Poison or dagger, nor refuse.
Rosamund her life must lose.

O, Jealousy is ever green,
Beware the vengeance
Of his queen.

From the poisoned cup she'll die
This, alas, I prophesy.

O, Jealousy is ever green,
Beware the vengeance
Of his queen.

A wave of nausea sweeps over me, each time I hear that persistent refrain.

O God, save me from Queen Eleanor. Yet even as I utter that prayer, I know there is no escape.

Elizabeth Barrett Browning of Colwall

ugust 12th. 1832.
This will be the last entry in my diary at Hope End. I know we must leave our beautiful home near Colwall.

I will try to contain my distress and encapsulate my whole life here in a few words. Perhaps my poems which dear Papa has had published might live after me; he even calls me the Poet-Laureate of Hope End.

Dear Papa will never know the extent of my anguish. He is a good man, known for rescuing local farm labourers from poverty out of his own pocket. Yet he will never share his feelings with us for he cannot release his emotions, not even when dear Mama died. He has never confided in me, his eldest daughter. I am now twenty-six years old, yet he can not bring himself to tell me that he has sold our home.

What will my future hold? Idyllic Hope End in its 500 acres of farmland, woodland and glorious park on the fringes of Colwall has been my world. I've lived here since I was three in this flamboyant, admittedly ostentatious mansion that papa built for us. Our neighbours, traditional county families who were used to an uneventful life on the borders between Hereford and Worcester were amazed to see our house replace the old seventeenth century mansion. If I thought there was another such in all England,' Papa would say, 'I would pull it down!' But there could never be another house like ours. The drawing room is so ornate it took seven years to decorate, whilst our Turkish minarets and central glass dome can be seen for miles around. Some were superstitious and swore our cast-iron domelets attracted all the lightning in the Malvern Hills.

I love those rippling hills. Bro, of course, has climbed up to British Camp. 'You should see the view, Ba,' he told me. 'The Hereford side looks like a lake ruffled by a stiff wind. The old Colwall hills are the first waves. You can actually see all of Colwall from here up, but it's impossible to spot the centre of the village, it's more like three hamlets stretching for six miles. There's a string of buildings along the main road in the valley and mostly big farms to the south-west. Oh Ba, I wish you could see the sunsets from up there, as the sun falls behind the Black Mountains.'

Dear Bro, he knows I tire easily. He knows I'll never climb those hills. The doctors have failed to diagnose my illness. Perhaps I injured my spine when at fifteen I fell from my pony, or perhaps my fainting spells and headaches are my way of escaping from doing what is expected of a young lady! How I hate sewing and embroidery—such a waste of time. And how tedious the conventional social round can be. Perhaps my 'illness' is my way of choosing what I want to do. Our house has such solid walls, the thickest in the county according to Papa, and yet I am often cold.

But in my little green room, the warmest in the house, I can read philosophy, novels, the classics and best of all, write poetry. My heart is in books and my experience in reveries—memories of a childhood in the summer house with Bro and our friends, the Peytons. I can no longer run down to the summer house, but must be wheeled in an invalid chair. My mind, however, is like a garden running wild. I look out of my window and my thoughts fly into the garden ...

past the lime, the lawn,
Which after sweeping broadly round the house,
Went trickling through the shrubberies in a stream
Of tender turf, and wore and lost itself
Among the acacias, over which you saw
The irregular line of elms by the deep lane
Which stopped the grounds and damned the overflow
Of arbutus and laurel.

Beyond are peacocks, ponds, fountains, grottoes, even an Alpine bridge. Papa has never done anything by halves and never doubted what he has done. He protects his trees like children and so he banished the deer which nibbled them. And as for his children, God help any young man who comes to court his daughters!

Look how he even treated Mr. Boyd—a scholar, already married and the height of respectability who only moved here for the sake of intellectual discussion with the vicar. Yet it was over a year before I was allowed to meet the man whose guidance on Greek I needed to stretch my mind. When, after a long correspondence, I did at last meet him, I was disturbed by his quenched and deadened eyes. I realised for the first time what it must be like to be blind. Mrs. Boyd is not intellectual. Still, she was grateful to me for reading to him and in return he lent me books from his vast classical library. What discussions we had about the inadequacies of visiting preachers! How sad that such innocent intellectual arguments should have caused comment in the village—I thought it most unkind of Mrs. Hill to ask Mrs. Boyd after church if she minded her husband spending so much time alone with Miss Barrett. Alas that the body should be assumed to prevail over the mind—how shocked Mr. Boyd would be. Dear Mr. Boyd! Even he has deserted me. The lease on his house ended in May and he and his wife have gone away. She writes the occasional letter to his dictation—but gone is my escape route to a teacher and friend.

Escape from Hope End? God forbid, for this is where I belong. We may be cut off from great events but we hear all about them. Here in the seclusion of my little green room I can admire Lord John Russell's efforts in piloting the Reform Bill through Parliament at Grey's instigation.

Our life is far from dull. For those who desire them, there are missionary meetings and Bible discussion groups in Colwall and Wellington Heath, but for myself, I prefer my own company, if I can't have Mr. Boyd's.

I must write to Mrs. Hill. I shall decline her invitation to read my poems at her Summer garden party, for she is sure to ask if I have heard from Mr. Boyd. Anyway, the weather is likely to be inclement and injurious to my health. I fear she will find some other diversion to amuse her guests for her ideas are as profuse as her teeth!

Then there is Miss Wall. I couldn't bear to reveal my innermost thoughts in front of that woman—a veritable Philistine. She would be there too, if only to embarrass me. How outrageous her behaviour has been to us. She had the audacity to walk round our house with her uncle and peer through our windows. They had heard rumours that it was for sale, but there can be no excuse for such insensitivity; even when Bro told Lane to turn them out or he would do so himself, they just laughed loudly.

Unfortunately there'll be no avoiding Miss Wall at church on Sunday. Papa always requires us to worship as a family at St. James's, Colwall. The Reverend Thomas Dean is not an eloquent preacher and I dread his sermons like thunder. However, the distance of the church from the village is a more likely reason for the small congregation. The bishop is to blame for that as lord of the manor. However, he does deign to visit us—annually, when he gives an address from the Stone, a symbol of infidelity if ever there was one. They say a terrible giant was walking on top of the Malverns when he looked down and saw another giant making love to his wife where Colwall now stands. So he threw the stone at them and there it stands to this day. Local folklore is fun but I prefer the legends of classical Greece.

Here in my little green room I can lose my sorrows in my studies. Hope End is the mellow landscape of my soul. I can never bear to leave it. No matter what my future holds, my spirit will always inhabit this place. I am part of the

Hills, vales, woods settled in silver mist
Farms, granges, doubled up amongst the hills
And cottage chimneys smoking from the woods.

Tom Spring of Fownhope

om Winter, my boy,' my mother used to say, 'if you want to get anywhere in this life, you'll have to get off your backside and walk there!'

This because I was born, in 1795, in Rudge End, a mile from the village of Fownhope and several more from Hereford, so walking became a way of life for us. The ancient milestone by the church was a constant reminder of our distance from town—the centre of the village was, in fact, exactly 6.5 miles and 56 yards from Hereford! I soon discovered that carrying messages to Hereford and back was a way of earning money for new boots and breeches.

Some of the older folk had never been out of Fownhope, others only went to town once a year, but the more adventurous would catch the market cart on Wednesdays. Anyway, there was plenty going on in the village—concerts, country dancing, penny readings and a good old sing song in the Green Man of an evening.

The climax of our year was the Club Walk on 29 May. This custom started in 1791, a few years before I was born, when the Fownhope Heart of Oak Friendly Society was founded. My dad was a member and paid his shilling, telling us it would mean we'd never starve. He was right too, for when he fell sick, the club leader came round and gave him 7 shillings sickness benefit. My mother wept her thanks.

I was eleven when Mr. Pocknell, the then club leader, asked me to rise before dawn on Club Walk Day to help him cut the mighty Fertility Bough. It was a great honour and I was so excited, I didn't sleep at all that night.

I had to run to keep up with him as he strode along the lane in the semi-darkness. We reached Capler Wood just as dawn filtered through the trees streaking the path with light. Only the birds were awake and in full voice when Mr. Pocknell chopped an enormous branch from a massive oak—and we had our Fertility Bough. We carried it back down the lane between us, past Oldstone Farm and up to the Tump. From there we could see the church spire, rising out of the early morning mist in the valley below. We had earned our rest.

'Give us a hand with the decorating, lad,' muttered Mr. Pocknell taking bundles of ribbons from his pockets.

That was the best part, sitting on the brow of the hill, our breeches wet with dew, our stomachs warmed by a flagon of cider from the nearby farm, and tying ribbons onto the bough—until it looked like a maypole!

As we worked he told me about the club meetings during the year. He didn't like disciplining the members, but he was a fair man who knew what had to be done. Didn't he have to fine his own cousin for coming into the club room wearing a hat? Disrespectful it was! Then there was that memorable meeting when Tom Tanner had come in drunk and challenged his neighbour to a fight. The other members had to forcibly remove him and Mr. Pocknell had had the unenviable task of calling on Tom later to collect a large fine. I also learnt—and I knew Mr. Pocknell regretted telling me but once the cider had loosened his tongue it was too late—that the blacksmith had been fined for being 'nasty' about my father

39

receiving sickness benefit. Such behaviour was strictly against the rules of the club.

'Now don't you bear any grudge, lad,' advised good old Mr. Pocknell. 'Be off now or you won't have time to decorate your own club stick before the walk begins.'

The procession was already assembling outside the Green Man. There, each boy wielded his stick in the firm belief that it was better than anyone else's and many leather leggings lost their shine in the scuffles that ensued. That was only the first test of the best stick. The Club walk leaves a trail of summer flowers: roses, pinks, sweet peas and marigolds all fall from the sticks every year. The wild flowers from the field and hedgerow are equally vulnerable. Bluebells, cowslips and oxeyed daisies wilt in protest at the length of the walk. Only sweet williams can be guaranteed to stay the course.

How proud I was, marching with my stick held high, behind the village brass band. In front of the band strode Mr. Pocknell with the oak bough followed by four members carrying the society's banner. The whole village turned out on Club Walk Day to follow the procession to the church.

It was always a squash in the church on that occasion. We all sang with gusto. We knew the three hymns: Stand up, Stand up for Jesus, Onward Christian Soldiers and Fight the Good Fight by heart. Many of us couldn't read so the hymns had to be the same every year—and the same went for the vicar's sermon! Still, there was always Johnny Goode's sneezing fit to look forward to; the pollen was sure to set him off. And then, of course, there were the refreshments.

The honorary members provided these during the walk which followed the service. They waited outside their front doors for us to march up their drives behind the brass band. The band deafened them with a tune or two, while our tongues drooled at the site of the barrels of beer and cider.

We boys had our fill, I can tell you! It wasn't just the flowers that were wilting by the time the walk ended at the Green Man. Tempers were frayed too, and an argument was to shape my destiny that Club Walk Day, before I had even reached my twelfth birthday.

It was Will Tyler who started it. He was sixteen and burly with it. He worked for the blacksmith who had been fined for belittling my father. The beer had made him aggressive and without warning he gave me a bloody nose. I retaliated with my fists and to everyone's amazement, including my own, I had soon knocked him to the ground.

I had earned a reputation. There was no stopping me thereafter. By the time I was twenty-two I had licked all the fighters in Herefordshire with my bare fists and become a professional prize fighter. My first professional match was well attended. My opponent was Stringer, an ugly, rough and weatherbeaten Yorky whose looks alone were formidable. But I was 6 foot of bone and muscle, a resilient 13 stone raring to go. Not that it was easy and it took me 29 rounds to floor him.

My prize money was all of 40 guineas and I was on the road to fame. But I considered that my surname had to go—Winter was no name for someone starting a promising career, so from then on I became Tom Spring.

As Tom Spring I won many fights. Opponents began to dread meeting the brute strength of my bare fists and before long it was time for me to take on John Langan, otherwise known as Irish Jack, for the championship of All England.

So many folk wanted to see us fight on Worcester Racecourse that they climbed on to the rigging of ships moored in the Severn so as to gain a clear view. The organizers put up stands for other spectators. No-one could have foretold that the fight would last 2 hours and 29 minutes, and all of 77 rounds. The sheer weight of the cheering crowds caused the stands to collapse, which was the worst moment of the fight for me and if any lives had been lost on my account, I could not have borne it. Thank God they all survived.

As for the Irish champion, I left him groggy, exhausted and, for a while, unconscious, whilst I became the Heavyweight Champion of All England, no less.

It was a good life till I got me a wife. 'Quit the fight game Tom,' said she. Anyway, better to go whilst the going's good, thought I. So I became landlord of a London tavern, but I pined for the land of cider and eagerly returned, as landlord of the Booth Hall Hotel in Hereford.

I reckon they were jealous in Fownhope. Well, you can understand it, can't you? If their famous villager was going to become a landlord, it ought to be in his own village—not in Hereford. That must be why the Green Man claims me as a former landlord. After all, Fownhope is where I belong.

So there I am in the Green Man's mural, baring my fists, ready for a fight. You'll recognize the black and white timbers of the inn in the painting too—but not its name. Before my time it was called the Naked Boy, probably after a local chimney sweep. In my day, folk thought the idea of a naked boy was rather rude, so they renamed it.

I've always had a certain respect for the place. The judge used to stop on his way from Gloucester to Hereford and hold his Petty Sessional Court there. He had his own special bedroom while down below in the cell his prisoners awaited his verdict, chained to iron bars. There was one judge, I remember, who was heard to say that a professional fighter was no better than a street brawler! Perhaps I was better off as landlord of the Booth Hall, all things considered. Not, mind you, that I could ever resist the invitation that hangs outside the Green Man. The landlord that thought that one up knew a thing or two.

> You travel far, you travel near
> It's here you find the best of beer,
> You pass the East, you pass the West,
> If you pass this, you pass the best.

They've stuck an ancient cider press on the site of Rudge End Farm to mark my birthplace, but I'd prefer it if you remember me in the taste of its produce!

Godric de Mapson of Goodrich

 killed my mother. She died at my birth. She was Saxon, that I know, but my guardian, Bishop Walter would never speak of my father. I was baptized Godric and you can't come more Saxon than that. Bred within me was hatred of the Welsh and suspicion of the Normans, despite the fact that my guardian, Bishop Walter of Lorraine, was Norman—as many lords of the manor were in those days.

It was the late William FitzOsbern, Earl of Hereford, who was to blame for all these Normans 'inheriting' our estates. Norman settlers were bribed to come and live out here on our exposed Marches. Much was made of their legal rights but many only 'inherited' estates when they'd killed off their English predecessors. This was the climate into which I was born— and it affected my whole life, though I didn't realise it till later.

Not that I was ill-used by the Normans. Quite the opposite: I owe them my education as a page in their households and my skill in riding, hawking, hunting and weaponry. I also served the bishop at table since 'the highest honour,' he would tell me, 'is to serve.'

The bishop had certainly served in his time. He used to be chaplain to Edward the Confessor's queen, Edith.

He was a good man and holy, yet seemingly troubled and never at ease in my presence. Yet he required me, when I was fourteen, to act as his squire.

It was in this capacity that I rode with him to the Welsh ford, a distance of over twenty miles.

'We're here, Godric!' Bishop Walter shouted. I could see no ford, only villeins' huts clustered round a manor house. Beyond were the wooded hills, where wattle and daub huts peeped through the trees, smudging the scene with smoke from their wood fires.

It was Michaelmas—the time when the manorial stewards totalled their accounts for their lord's inspection. I had to listen patiently to the bishop's inquiries about his 500 acres worked by two ox-teams, his fourteen acres of meadows and his two enclosed woods. I wasn't really interested; I wanted to see the Welsh ford. My glance wandered to the harvested fields where cattle grazed while the villagers ploughed and harrowed the fallow land. Clearly, the reeve who managed the estate for the bishop did a good job.

'No-one is late for haymaking or takes timber from the woods here without permission,' he told the bishop, who seemed to be more concerned about the state of some of the cottages and left strict instructions that they were not to be allowed to fall into disrepair.

At last it was time to see the Welsh ford. It was a mere thousand paces from the village. I had to restrain my disappointment: were these slippery stones really the chief highway into the Marches and Wales since Roman times?

'The land across the river is no longer Welsh,' explained Bishop Walter, 'we've fought hard to keep that hill out of their grasp.' He paused as though he wanted to say more and then suddenly added, grudgingly, 'Taldus who held that hill when you were born, bravely defended it.'

We dismounted and I stood awkwardly holding the reins of our horses. He remained silent, listening to the voice of the river, his

head bowed as though in respect. Finally he spoke. 'It shames me to tell you this, Godric, but tell you I must.' Then he lapsed into silence.

'Tell me what, sir?'

'What happened here fifteen years ago. There was a wood nymph, moving with angel-grace gathering daisies on yonder bank. God forgive me ...' He broke off in tears. I was horrified, I had never seen him weep before. 'I didn't know, Godric, I had no idea who she was ... I thought she was a servant, for she was unattended, completely alone. My blood was hot; I was an ambitious young cleric, newly elevated to a bishopric. Everything I wanted seemed to fall into my lap—and I wanted her. So I galloped across the ford and threw myself from my horse on to the girl—I hear her screams still in my worst nightmares.'

'No more my lord, I beseech you,' I begged, desperate to relieve my own embarrassment, 'keep this for your confessor.'

'You still don't realise Godric, do you? Beneath yonder maple tree, you were conceived, for that was where I raped your mother.'

'My mother?'

He nodded, 'And I am your father, but you do not bear my name. Instead I called you Mapson, after the maple tree under which we lay.'

'And my mother ... who was she?'

I thought he would never answer. Then suddenly he spoke and there was no stopping him. 'The wife of Taldus of Hülle! She didn't know who I was until she recognized me at my consecration in Hereford Cathedral. It was lit with a thousand candles, the air heavy with incense, my moment of glory—and in she walks on her husband's arm and faints at the sight of me. She had hidden her shame from Taldus until that moment.'

I opened my mouth to speak and then shut it again. I was so confused. For a second I thought he was full of self-pity because she had spoilt his great day, but no, it was self-recrimination that he felt for the suffering he had inflicted on her. He was choking on the words. 'She died in childbirth for my sin.'

And so I learnt how Taldus couldn't bear the sight of me and sent me in the care of my wet nurse to Bishop Walter, who had raised me as Godric Mapson, the son of a maple tree! I would be a laughing stock if that went round, so when Bishop Walter suggested we put the past behind us and never speak of it again, I readily agreed. Anyway, I couldn't stand any more. I had glimpsed the torment of his soul and was helpless to ease it. What could I say? I couldn't pretend to care for the mother whom I had never known. Neither could I imagine this gentle bishop who abhorred violence, forcing himself on any woman, be she lady or servant. I told myself that his irrepressible passion was love not lust and reminded myself of the times he had condemned violence, indeed resisted the tyranny of King William and had his lands ravaged in consequence. 'The king is a strict ruler and puts down all disorder with a strict hand,' Bishop Walter would say, 'but he is stern beyond bounds to those who withstand his will.' Many were the tales he told to prove this point.

One such incident took on a new significance now that I knew, that I, like the king, was a bastard. It happened before I was born, in Alençon, where the inhabitants unwisely mocked William because he was a bastard whose mother was a tanner's daughter. They hung hides on their city wall and beat them, crying 'tanner' as William rode by. He had his revenge and cut off the hands and feet of thirty-two of those unfortunate citizens.

It was a tale that made Bishop Walter (I couldn't call him 'Father' even in private) wince. Yet he persistently told it to remind himself of the consequences of the king's wrath, lest he incur it unnecessarily.

Of such matters he encouraged me to talk, but of parentage I must never speak. Neither could I presume to ask if he himself would dub me knight—that was usually a proud occasion for father and son. As it happened, I received that honour from the king.

We had ridden to London, to Westminster when the earth was hard with frost, for the funeral of the dowager Queen Edith, whose chaplain Bishop Walter had once been. Many clerics attended the occasion, including the Abbot of Winchcombe, whose penetrating gaze somewhat unnerved me. Did he know I was named after a maple tree? I blushed self-consciously, but then the king arrived with all his retinue. I had never seen him before and I was impressed. His stern countenance was so awesome, he exuded authority; even his armour couldn't conceal his muscular strength.

The day following that ceremonial funeral, I knelt before the king. The morning was crisp and the earth touched lightly with snow, but trumpet flourishes and minstrels' music filled the air while several other knights helped me on with my armour. How proud I was of my horse and armour—they were worth all of 23 cows. My sword I received from the king, accompanied by a heavy blow, delivered with the flat of his hand on my neck.

After feeling the impact of the strongest hand in England, it was all I could do to leap on my horse and charge at the quintaine to show my prowess as a horseman and potential warrior. I was surprised to find myself wishing that my mother could have been there to see me in all my glory, yet would she have been proud of one whose conception and birth had destroyed her?

Such thoughts I kept to myself and indeed the only person with whom I might have shared them was taken from me in 1079, when Bishop Walter died in circumstances that are painful for me to recall. For, alas, inside that compassionate man dwelt an uncontrollable sexual appetite, ironically unrecognized by myself. He had become completely infatuated with a servant girl, the fair Aelfwynn, who worked in his palace as a seamstress. She was skilled at needlework and was engaged in making and mending the bishop's robes. I was therefore surprised to discover one day that she had been been relegated to the more menial tasks of housecleaning, clearing and laying fires—tasks which, I subsequently discovered, removed her from the bishop's immediate presence and out of temptation's way.

It seemed, however, that he came upon her unexpectedly, alone, in a room where she was moving the furniture so that she might sweep the floor. His emotions aroused at the sight of her, he ripped open her bodice but never succeeded with his intentions, for she stabbed him with the scissors which she still carried from her sewing days.

I had just stabled my horse and was in the courtyard when I heard her shrieks. I ran, with others of his household towards that eerie sound. A terrible sight met our eyes: he lay on the floor with the scissors in his body, the blood seeping through his robe, while the girl, still clutching her torn gown to her breasts, screamed hysterically.

I knelt at his side, wincing at his pain as I drew the scissors from the wound.

'Godric, my son, he gasped, 'pray that I may be forgiven.'

And so I was alone in the world—but hadn't I always been alone, for I had never really known this man who had told me he was my father. What a piece of work he was, a tangle of lust and piety—a riddle I could never solve. The more I thought about him, the greater was my confusion. My grasp on the real world was becoming tenuous—and I sank into a fever. Not until I recovered did I realise that sickness had prevented me from joining the king's army in Normandy.

Meanwhile, Robert Losinga had arrived from Lorraine to become our new bishop. From him I learnt of the king's problems in Normandy, of his terrible battle with his rebellious son Robert who had wounded him in the hand. Bishop Losinga told how the king's horse had been slaughtered under him and how the man who brought him another was immediately killed by a bolt from a crossbow. I dearly wished I could have been part of the fray and longed to serve my king in battle.

Gradually I regained my strength. Soon I was able to ride over to the Welsh ford and listen to the voice of the river that had witnessed my conception. I had no family but I had that place. I couldn't even recall Bishop Walter's face, though he had been dead barely two years, but the wind in the trees whispered of the mother I had never known and the river echoed her rippling laughter.

The thud of hooves broke into my thoughts. Here was a messenger with a writ from the king. I couldn't believe what I read: 'William the King greets all his liegemen well. And I make known to you that I have granted Godric Mapson all the land of Hülle as fully and as completely with the right to hold a legal court, as his father Taldus had it under Edward. And I command Godric Mapson, son of Taldus, to build a castle on the hill to protect the Welsh ford. And I will not permit any man to deprive him of it on the penalty of losing my friendship.'

And so, I, Godric Mapson had seemingly acquired a new father, and his estate. Only a fool disobeyed the Conqueror—I hadn't forgotten Bishop Walter's warning. If the king declared I was the son of Taldus, so be it, and if he wanted a castle, I must build it.

I looked with new eyes at the hill rising above the river; it was mine, all mine. I listened with new ears to the rushing water rejoicing in its new master. My castle would stand in glorious isolation, high on the rocky hill overhanging the river above the ford. It wouldn't take long; a timber palisade and watch tower complete with bank and ditch could be built in twelve weeks.

Apparently news had already spread that Hülle had a new lord and a lord who held the land by right. Folk at the manor were glad to welcome the son of Taldus for the Abbot of Winchcombe had prepared them for my arrival. They were eager to build my castle, though they had no choice, of course, for they owed me their allegiance.

How hard they worked and I with them. The day after we finished the ditch stands out in my memory. The previous afternoon, when urging my horse up the steep hill to the site of my castle, I had overtaken the reeve's wife and several other women taking bread and flagons of mead to their men. With difficulty I took plump mistress Tubbing and her provisions onto my horse. 'Thank you, sir,' she puffed, 'they'll be glad of some refreshment I'll be bound.' They had worked all that day and through the night, digging the ditch by the light of burning torches.

What a thrill to see that the ditch was finished and that work had begun on the stockade, for while some were digging, others had axed the trees and stacked the timber ready to make a stockade of wooden stakes round my wooden keep.

Alas, every triumph has its price: one of my villeins had broken his back. Reeve Tubbing's broad back bent in uncharacteristic concern over the agonised face told it all: the man would never walk again—pray God, he wouldn't see morning. However, whatever the price, the castle must be built.

Oh, I was proud, of both my castle and my land of Hülle, or Goda's reich, but that was before William the Bastard visited me in that year of Our Lord, 1081.

He was on his way to St. David's in Wales—a pilgrimage, according to the Abbot of Winchcombe, but others said it was more like a display of strength to impress the newly installed Rhys ap Tewdr with whom he had come to a financial agreement. The king was broader and stouter than I remembered, and it required a strong horse to carry him. His voice was as strong as his thighs, with which he controlled his horse.

'Godric Mapson,' he bellowed, 'this is a fine site for a castle. I need castles along my Marches—but not wooden castles, for they are quickly built and quickly burnt down. Build a strong stone castle, Godric, and hold it with a strong hand!'

'It shall be done my lord,' I heard myself say, though I wondered how. My men were exhausted with building a wooden keep, but we were all more terrified of the king than of the Welsh. Terrible stories of his ruthless quelling of rebellion in the north had reached us—thousands of people had starved to death through his burning their corn and cattle to ashes in his wrath. My men would build his stone castle or die in the attempt.

'Stay with Godric, Abbot, give him guidance and bring stone masons from the city,' were his parting words as the gold lions of Normandy were raised. I was left only with the rippled horse-hooved mud to remind me of the visit.

Meanwhile, Reeve Tubbing was encouraging the men to return to work on the stockade. They did so, half-heartedly.

'There's wisdom in the king's command, my son,' the abbot declared, sensing my resentment.

'Well might they call him the Bastard.' I retorted and regretted my indiscretion instantly. It could cost me my life.

The abbot only smiled, 'Bastards make the best leaders, Godric. They learn to cope from birth, as you have done in the belief that you were a bastard, though I can tell you now that your father Taldus told on his death-bed how he had disowned you—out of anger and jealousy. Your mother never told of her ordeal on the river bank till she recognized her attacker in his bishop's robes at his consecration. After that, Taldus couldn't bear her near him. She died, not of childbirth—but of grief.'

'But how can you prove I am his son?'

'I knew the first time I saw you, when you were dubbed knight at Westminster. It was as though Taldus had been reborn: the likeness was unmistakable and I told the king as much.'

I turned away in disappointment: that wasn't proof. 'Send the men home, Master Reeve, they all need a night's sleep. There's no fear of attack with the king in the area. Bring them all back at dawn.'

They went and the abbot with them, tending the injured man in the cart and I was alone with two truths which must be faced: I could never know for certain who was my father and my castle was a failure because it was not built of stone.

The Welsh wind blew from the hostile mountains through the gaps in my timbered tower. I climbed to the top of the keep and watched the valley far below drift into night. It was though the land was cut away beneath me and dropped into the silver moonlit river snaking round my mountain. I seemed suspended in the night sky; master of the horizon on every side.

I was lord of my own destiny, son of no man. I swore to God that I would build a square keep here, with arrow slits in its walls and a moat hewn out of solid rock. Under my keep there was to be a vaulted pitch-black dungeon where prisoners would quake at the name of Godric Mapson!

Wearily I descended the keep, a new found confidence relaxing my limbs. I sank onto the timbered floor, fighting ... sleep ...

It smells in the dungeon—of urine and damp; raucous coughing wracks the chest of my prisoner. The flame of my torch flickers over a face hedged with mud-tangled hair and filthy beard—yet there is something eerily familiar about it.

'Am I your son?' I hear myself shout. 'Why have you disowned me?' I strike him again, flinching at a pain that is my own. His face melts under my fists, mud-tangled hair thins to wisps of grey. He speaks with the voice of Bishop Walter. 'Godric, my son, forgive me!'

There are scissors in my hand. Have I stabbed my own father? I recoil in horror. Have I killed him? His cries ring in my ears as I run up the stone steps and on to the battlements. I hurl myself over the wall—and fall, fall, fall towards the river where I feel the water washing away the troubles of both my fathers.

The rain wakes me: the gentle Herefordshire rain, not the driving Welsh sleet. It will fall through centuries to come on my castle, the invincible stone guardian of the border that I will build here. It shall be Godric's Castle and carry my name, and mine alone, into posterity.

Henrietta Webb of Hardwicke

icars' wives have to share their husbands with God but I have to share mine with the entire galaxy too!

I suppose I should have expected it. Thomas had been star-struck since childhood. At sixteen he was writing 'I had much practice in viewing the heavens' in his precious notebook. A month afterwards he had invented a new telescope! Astronomy has always been his first love and he's kept notebooks on the Moon and stars in all the forty odd years I've known him.

In some ways we were opposites, Thomas and I. He was an only son whilst I came from a large family and couldn't stand on ceremony. 'You'll have to mind your manners, Henrietta my girl,' my mother would say, 'if you're going up to Tretire Vicarage. Take your water colours to show to the Vicar!' The Reverend John Webb had an eligible son; a prospective daughter-in-law must be seen to be accomplished.

The vicar made polite noises over my paintings before announcing that his son had just graduated from Oxford with mathematical honours. We had barely uttered our congratulations to the gifted sibling before his father proudly added that Thomas was shortly to be ordained deacon.

Afterwards I danced the first quadrille with Thomas. It was comforting to discover that the Brain of Tretire had two left feet. I rashly promised to teach him the steps.

'Thank you, Miss Wyatt for your patience and good humour,' he said and took me into supper. We talked, mostly about astronomy which meant I mostly listened. Then he asked what my interests were.

'Switzerland,' I breathed, 'I've always wanted to sketch Chillon Castle and capture its eternal spirit on paper.'

His eyes lit up. He had found a kindred spirit. 'You've been reading Byron,' he said.

How typical that Colonel Egerton should then lean across the table to regale us with how he'd killed a viper with a stick. 'Ripped it open I did,' he guffawed, 'and what do you think was inside? Not one mouse, but two!'

A week later Thomas came to visit us. He looked unusually apprehensive, but there was no need. Father accepted his means and his prospects and we were to be married. Later I suspect my father regretted his instant acceptance on my behalf. My father-in-law's reaction was more pointed. 'Matrimony was ordained for the procreation of children' became his parting shot after every visit. God, it appeared, had denied us issue.

It wasn't God, of course—it was Thomas. It wasn't appropriate to explain. The night may have been made for loving, but Thomas spent it in the garden. Below stairs it was common knowledge he had a relationship with the stars in his canvas tent, and by the time we moved to Hardwicke Vicarage in the early 1850's we were generally accepted as a childless couple.

We were the first to live in Hardwicke's new vicarage which had only just been built, along with the church, so that Hardwicke would no longer be regarded as part of Clifford. The first vicar had stayed with relatives in the locality and when he died four years after his induction, Thomas was invited to succeed him.

I was amazed by the house. It was so modern by mid-nineteenth century standards. It was nice to be fashionable, but without a basement or attic where was I going to put the servants? They would have to go on the upper floor—right at the back.

'We need space, Thomas,' I told him, 'even if we don't have children, so my family can visit.' I was thinking particularly of my pretty nieces, Helen and Louisa Wyatt. They were like daughters to me. There were nine children in their family so they loved coming to stay with Aunt Henrietta, who, I can confess, was given to spoiling them.

'Allocate the rooms how you wish, my dear,' was all I gained from Thomas.

I so enjoyed furnishing and equipping our new home. We planned to entertain on a lavish scale for Thomas enjoyed company in the daylight hours. In the early evening, before the stars were fully out, he was a splendid host. Hardwicke Vicarage exuded hospitality. Our social set consisted of country gentry accustomed to circulating from one house to another to enjoy dinner and music in the drawing room. Every one of my 200 wine glasses were regularly used at our parties and the evening would often end with a visit to the observatory in the garden.

What a pleasure it was to see my beautiful niece Helen commanding the attention of the young men! I can see her now in her elegant blue dress being led into the garden by that handsome young curate, Francis Kilvert. 'They're going to look at the moon,' Thomas had remarked. If you believe they're interested in your astronomy, Thomas, you're sadly mistaken, I remember thinking to myself.

Poor Francis, barely a month after he had married another, he became very ill. Thomas went to visit him and took gifts from me. They included one of my sketches of Chillon Castle and a lampshade ornamented with dried flowers, leaves and ferns which I had fastened between perforated card and net. Tragically, Francis died soon after Thomas's visit. He left no children. His widow, Elizabeth, remains inconsolable; she will never marry again.

Thomas and I have been more fortunate. We have lived for thirty years in this vicarage, here at Hardwicke. Thomas calls it an 'extensive parish' in that there are just three buildings at its centre: the

church, the vicarage and the Royal Oak inn, whilst the farms are scattered hither and thither. But his way of life and this parish have allowed him plenty of time to become famous in his own right—as the Father of Amateur Astronomy.

He has brought the heavens to the people—if not to his wife! He is the talk of the village, the county, even the nation, for he has generated so much public interest throughout the country with his books and magazine articles. His book *Celestial Objects* has become a best seller, a classic some say. Enthusiasts like that ingratiating Reverend Cooper Key from Stretton Sugwas and that tedious headmaster, Mr. Georth With from Hereford's Bluecoat School, never cease telling me how much they value my husband's encouragement and help.

I can hear Reverend Key now, saying to Thomas, 'It doesn't seem right that with all your fame you should be vicar of a tiny parish. You really ought to be at St. Paul's in London.'

Thomas replied, 'If they built something like St. Paul's on the estate here, I might consider it!'

That was typical. We both loved the tranquil beauty of our countryside. If he had to arrange for a special delivery of mail from Hereford to cope with his massive correspondence, it was the price he paid for fame in remote Herefordshire. He also found the time to edit his father's work on the memorials of the Civil War in Herefordshire, this wonderful county of ours.

Part of the countryside indeed came into our house—on our parishioners' muddy boots. In they tramped, straight from the fields, through my carpeted hallway and into his study.

'It won't do, Thomas' I said. 'That carpet will be ruined. Your study needs an outer back door. Then they can go round the back way.'

He readily agreed for that way he would be less disturbed in the front garden where stood the precious telescope in its canvas shelter or observatory. There he spent most evenings and nights, studying the sky with easy access to his library of 3,000 books and precious notebooks.

I'm welcome to use his library too, of course. I just don't have the time, though, for there are parties and the church bazaar to organise, servants to supervise, parish meetings to attend, the sick to visit; I've even been asked to give my lecture on Switzerland again. Then there is my painting. 'The stars are dead, Thomas,' I say, but he doesn't hear. 'We have had our three score years and ten. I want to use the rest of my days painting the living wonders of nature.'

I saw an unusual water bird the other day. I've painted it on the drawing room door. 'What is it, Etta?' our friends ask. They guess indiscriminately: Heron? Bittern? Dunlin? Swan? They suspect I've invented it, but I haven't. I saw it, I, alone. It's my bird. I shall call it an Ettawebb.

He has given the world *Celestial Objects*. I am more than the woman behind a great man who could not give me children. I am the woman who gave the world the Ettawebb!

Edith Oldecriste of Hereford

ack and side, go bare, go bare,
Both hand and foot go cold,
But belly, God send thee good ale
   enough.
Whether it be new or old!

   I am cold but ale will warm me.
I am not mad. 'Tis all the other folk. Didn't I tell 'em
the babe was doomed? Didn't I take juniper berries,
pennyroyal and tansy and say magic words to get me a
miscarriage?
   A gruelling birth it was, in mid-winter, in the lean
part of the year when we live on salted beef and
smoked bacon, dried peas and beans and the remains
of last year's wheat or rye. Oh, how I long for May
Day, for light, warmth and fresh food—and the clatter
of the fair folk in Hereford streets. Bring back the rich
merchants and pedlars arriving with their embroid-
eries, silks and jewels!
   But 'tis not May, 'tis only mid-March and snow-
laden winds sweep across from Wales ... which is why
I disobey my husband Robert, master smithy though
he be, and carry my dying child to warm her by his
furnace. Ale has given me my courage.
   But what is this, the child is cold and stiff? She no
longer cries. She is dead before the leaping flames can

warm her. Golden tongues lick the shadows. If this is the fire of Hell then it's brighter than icy Heaven with a priest mumbling over a cold shallow grave dug with the sexton's sweat in frozen earth.

'Give me the bellows.' I yell at the sallow-faced apprentice, for the flames must splutter greedily for my child. He is frightened of Edith Furiosa and lays the bellows at my feet while shouting for the master. Robert is outside, counting the horseshoes that he is obliged to make from the king's iron for the garrison at the castle.

I dip my finger in the charcoal that lies on the cobbled floor and make a black cross on her cold forehead, then, wrapping her blood-soaked blanket in my own shawl, I toss her into the flames and work the bellows to make the fire devour her.

'Our Father, which art in Heaven ...' I pause ... is he in Hell too? Why am I so confused?

'What devilish deed is this, wife?' yells Robert, running to peer in disbelief into the furnace before he vomits. Why blame me when 'tis he who is to blame? Had he not taken me in my bed when I was seven months with child, I would surely have gone my full time. Even as I lay with him, I knew he was hankering after Gossip Turnbull.

My rage gives me strength and spitting and cursing, I strike him with the bellows. His face is charcoal-smudged with the rain of my fury. If I could lift the anvil I'd strike him with that. 'O lecherous toad,' I shriek, 'God has made our child suffer for your sin!' My nails dig into the rough skin of his hands as he wrests the bellows from my grasp. My body may be weak from childbirth, but my spirit is strong from ale and I kick out at him and laugh hysterically as he squirms on the cobbles.

'Grab her by the hair, Tom!' pants he to his apprentice, who bravely makes a bid for my unkempt plait. The lying-in woman is on the scene now, crying out that I have murdered my child and comes at me like a demented demon. My energy leaves me, my legs give way, I feel my hair is being pulled out and then I am wrapped

in the coarse hair of a rough cloak. I can see nothing through the stifling cloth but can easily hear Gossip Turnbull's piercing pleas for me to repent and quit the ale-house. That woman deserves the ducking-stool for her interference, though everyone else thinks she's a saint.

How long have I lain in my bed since I heard those cries—I do not know. I am weak from blood-letting. They give me sleep-wort and poppy but little ale. Robert refuses to sleep with me, for he says I wake cursing and clawing at him with my hands.

Is this my mother I see bending over me, wiping my face with her kerchief? I notice her gown smells of stale stew. She may be old but she has more strength in her little finger than I in my whole body and I hate her for it, and for her simpering morality. She does not fear the Day of Judgement. Her hand rests on my breast and I seize the chance to sink my teeth into her finger as I have a dog's lust for her bone. Her cries bring Robert who forces my jaws apart to release her savaged digit.

'What ails thee, Edith?' she sobs.

''Tis the demons in her, mother,' Robert insists, 'See she hath claws like a cat! Bind her, we must!'

So in comes Gossip Turnbull and her bloated sister, the miller's wife, with woollen bindings. Trussed up I am, like a chicken, and my throat's so dry I can barely scream.

'You'll do well to measure her,' declares the Gossip, parading her bogus authority.

'What do I do?' asks my pathetic spouse.

'Measure her height and light a candle of that length before the Holy Cross in the cathedral,' says she.

A fat lot of good that would do me—the shoemaker's mother would be more likely to find a cure. 'I want the old cobblerwoman,' I whisper.

'Not that witch!' breathes Gossip and crosses herself.

And so they fetch the chandler with his string. He becomes all excited because the string breaks at just the proper length while he is measuring me. The fool, he's more superstitious than any witch!

'Into the basket with you, my dear!' says Robert, who gets the chandler to help lift me into a large basket. Then they load me into the cart used for bringing the charcoal from the forest.

My view is restricted for I am lying tied up and on my back in the basket. My bones ache as the cart bumps over cobbles. I don't know which is worse—the cobbles or the potholes when the lane becomes an earthen track. I can only look up at the new city wall of which our burgesses are so proud. It has six great stone gatehouses and they say there's not a stronger walled town in all England. All those stones may keep out the Welsh but not the smell of the sewerage in the city ditch outside the wall. Above the sound of chipping stone I can hear some men on the wall shouting to each other—something about a witch in a cart.

My mind is suddenly lucid. I recognize the voice of the master mason rebuking his men for insulting the wife of Master Oldecriste, the respected master ironmonger. 'May God bless Mistress Edith,' he calls, 'and mend her mind.'

'She be drunk, not sick,' Robert answers, trying to protect himself from the thought of being wedded to a wife touched by an evil spirit.

We reach the market square and I wonder who's in the stocks. We stop and I hear the squeal of the pigs which are in the way. Pigs are always a nuisance here, wandering with chickens through the rubbish and sweepings from the stables, looking for food. Someone has made a pig-sty in the middle of the street, judging by Robert's ill-tempered comments caused by the delay.

We are halted again, this time outside the shoemaker's shop. I know, though I can't raise myself to see, that the old cobblerwoman will be sitting on a stool outside, beside the benches displaying the shoes. Inside, in the workroom, her son the cordwainer and his apprentice will be making shoes. If only I could raise myself and beg her for a cure. But I don't have the chance, for with a jolt we're on the move again, and soon approach the cathedral.

Already I sense the presence of spirits rising from the city grave-yard, then I see the West end of the mighty cathedral blotting out the sun, like a monster waiting to swallow me up. My screams bring forth the clergy, and prayers are muttered over me as I'm carried inside, along with my measured-candle dedicated to the Holy Cross.

The lofty roof and massive tall pillars of the nave rise in digni-fied outrage at such treatment. They answer my shrieking immediately, and I relax for the spirits in the pillars understand me. Lying prostrate in my basket my eyes can follow each pillar to the very top without ricking my neck. Those near the West door wear zig-zag hats.

Then Gossip Turnbull interrupts my reverie. 'There's the font, Edith, where you were baptized. Pray God you haven't forgotten how your parents renounced the devil on your behalf.' May she stick her head in it and be eaten by the lions carved round its base!

I have left the zig-zag hatted pillars behind now. We are almost at the chancel where the pillars have donned frilly head-pieces, as though in deference to the altar beyond. There's a feeling of infinite space being channelled into the lofty framework of the tower above me—I think of the space as an escape, though I know I'm trapped in this giant stone cage. I fear I shall freeze to death, for I can no longer feel my hands or feet. My basket is put down in front of the altar.

'Pray to the Holy Cross, my dear,' says Robert. 'You won't be alone for I'm leaving these two good women to look after you.' I might have known it—Gossip Turnbull and her insufferable sister. They'll not be doing it for nothing, that's for sure!

I summon the energy to scream in frustration. God answers, but I can't distinguish His voice from mine in the echoing void and make myself hoarse trying to tell Him so.

'Quiet, Edith,' hisses the Gossip. 'The choir are trying to practise for Palm Sunday.'

Now a fat cleric is bellowing at me. 'You won't stop her,' Robert tells him pathetically. Why don't they talk to me, not over me? It's all so confusing.

The fat cleric turns out to be William de Montfort, a precentor of the cathedral, who takes it upon himself to explain the cause of my madness to Robert. I stop screaming to listen, only to learn that I am suffering from a seizure. Who or what has seized me? Is it the Devil? I open my mouth to scream again, but close it suddenly on seeing the pale face of a young priest bent over mine.

He speaks, not like the others to a mad woman, but softly as though he's sharing a confidence with a friend. 'Seek St. Thomas's help, Mistress Edith,' he whispers, 'be measured by him. Your hope of recovery will be greater if St. Thomas Cantilupe intercedes.'

I don't know what he means, but I no longer feel afraid and submit quietly to being carried to where the remains of St. Thomas lie—in the Chapel of the Blessed Virgin.

Beneath arches carved with dragons, crowned heads and grotesque creatures supported on slender pillars, I feel strangely relaxed and mesmerised by the rich colour of the pointed windows. 'Tis like being in a small church instead of a great cathedral. The singing of the choir is now far away, angelic voices floating in space.

The Gossip interrupts by urging the young priest to tell me about St. Thomas, then even she stops whittling to listen.

He speaks of our late bishop with such affection, as though the man still lives even though he's been dead five years. 'Would that he had never made that visit to the Pope in Italy,' he sighs, 'he was already a sick man. Nowhere was his loss felt more than here in Hereford, but we must suffer what God inflicts upon us. Yet though we could not have him alive, it is our comfort to have him dead. Here in this chest, Mistress Edith, lie his relics. His bones were separated from his flesh and brought here, together with his head and his heart. These his relics are the most precious treasure in Hereford Cathedral and here they lie in the chapel of Our Blessed Lady, to whom in both life and death he was so singularly devoted. You will be one of the last to see them in this chapel, Mistress Edith, for next week they will be moved to his glorious new tomb in the north transept.'

As I listen to this tribute to the old bishop, I find myself wondering what he would think of his proposed move to a place which they say is just like Westminster Abbey. St. Thomas, as they now insist on calling our late ugly bishop with his large nose and red hair, was such a humble man. It was rumoured that he always wore a rough hair shirt next to his skin as penance. What would he think of so grand a resting-place? I remember how he would bring the poor in from outside his palace gates to fill up the empty places at his dinner table. I was angry, I recall, that beggars dined with the bishop when the master ironmonger and his wife went uninvited.

As I ponder, the day draws on and in the evening I am carried back to the main body of the cathedral. The candle at my head which was lit in the Lady Chapel goes out and it seems so dark.

Tomorrow Robert will take the other candle to Wisteston where there's another Holy Cross. That measured by the chandler will be positioned by my head for lighting tomorrow morning. How desperate the poor man is!

I know he is ashamed of his mad wife, indeed I cry, though quietly for I don't wish to wake Gossip and her sister asleep on mats beside me. I cannot bear the sight of her false face, all contrived compassion, while she schemes to succeed me as Mistress Oldecriste. To banish her image I visualise the old bishop's stern countenance and giggle in spite of myself at his grotesque nose. 'You will not reject me,' I say to him, 'for like Our Lord, you dined with sinners.'

I sleep more soundly than I have for days. When I awake, the older priest has arrived to celebrate Mass. He has to walk round the basket in which I lie, still bound. It is early morning, but still dark even though all the lamps and candles, bar that now by my head, have been lit.

In the background I hear a noise. It sounds like the murmur of a great river, but it gains in loudness. Is the Wye about to submerge the cathedral? I can hear nothing else and I work to try to release my hands that I may press them to my ears. The noise appears to split the air; it seems that all the candles go out, even those on the altar and I seem to be in darkness for time without end. Then suddenly a blinding flash lights the candle standing at my head.

I hear the priest cry. 'Behold, a miracle—the furiosa's candle is lit! That is the very wick made of the thread that measured her to the Saint.'

A strange radiance warms my body. I see St. Thomas standing before me, his white robes glowing so transparently that I can see right through to his rough hair shirt that hangs round his knees. His hands are outstretched, and his words which only I can hear echo in my heart.

So intense is my desire to grasp his hands that at last I break the cords which bind me and stand up of my own accord. My legs are no longer weak, my mind is clear and tranquil. 'Where is this St. Thomas that bids me be well?' I ask in a voice no longer rasping, but sweet and gentle, for I can no longer see him, yet feel he is at my side.

I look around and recognise Dom Gilbert, procurator of the cathedral, and my good neighbour, Mistress Turnbull and her sister, worthy souls who have attended me during my illness. I can't see the young priest and realise I won't in this life, but feel him also at my side as I walk with with my friends to the Lady Chapel to pray before the Relics of the Blessed Thomas. The choir comes too, drawn by the clamour, and precedes us singing Te Deum in thanksgiving for my cure, whilst the great bells of the cathedral are rung in celebration.

Robert, my ever faithful and loving husband, hears them as he returns from Wisteston. A messenger greets him with news of the cause even before he enters the city walls. Before long he is at my side, the West doors are flung open and there on Robert's arm, I stand as though we were newly wed, against cathedral stone blushing in the welcome warmth of a pale sun.

'See!' cries William the precentor to the gathering crowds summoned by the bells. 'Here is Edith Furiosa made well by our St. Thomas. This is his first miracle—Praise God there will be many more!' He lowers his voice and winks at his fellow clergy, 'At just the right time too, to coincide with the translation of the shrine to the north transept and the celebration of Easter.'

Word soon spread throughout Herefordshire and beyond. The merchant on his business round talks of my cure; the peasant who passes strangers as he hurries homewards hears wondrous rumours of the woman with the furious frenzy, healed by St. Thomas Cantilupe in Hereford Cathedral.

Word reaches my former friend, poor Juliana, paralysed for nine years since childbirth. She is placed, like me, in a basket by the saints' relics where, like me, she sees St. Thomas who restores her limbs to full and perfect use.

Oh, there will be much bell-ringing and Te Deum singing in the weeks and months ahead, with the sick lying about the cathedral waiting to be cured. Flurries of miracles will occur in the north transept where the Saint's bones will lie. Crowds will flock to the shrine and the cathedral will become rich from the gifts of visitors.

But mine was the first miracle.

The Muzzled Bear of Kilpeck

ho am I? What am I? A muzzled bear cast in stone? My muzzle fastened by a pair of human heads? Just one of those uncouth figures Saxon and Norman masons habitually placed on keystones and friezes. Just another gargoyle grimacing from the outside wall of Kilpeck Church in remote rural Herefordshire. Or am I more?

Damn you Hugh de Kilpeck! Why did you give your master mason licence to create me?

Keeper of the royal forest you might have been, but you had no right to play God in the Primeval Forest and conjure monsters out of stone. Yours was the ultimate responsibility. 'Add an Agnus Dei and a Garden of Eden over the south doorway for good measure!' was your advice to your sculptor, 'and the Almighty will be appeased!'

But what of us? The tormented creatures your savage imagination has conceived out of shapeless nightmare?

Upturned human faces use inane epithets to describe our agony. 'Fascinating!' 'Unique!' and of course, 'Romanesque' and 'grotesque' gleaned from their guide books.

'One of the most important medieval sites in England' pronounces an official of English Heritage who has come to survey the church and castle.

'A little fairy church at the foot of a crumbling castle' declares a budding poet before she scrambles up the mound to the west of the church to take a look at the castle. Two crumbling walls are all that she sees.

I know about the castle for we know many things about our makers. Their words and reactions are moulded in our stone. The mortal hands that made us have turned to dust but we endure to mock them—monstrous effigies that can never escape our ugliness—can never die.

We have outlasted the mighty castle. How often I have heard the grumbling masons bemoaning their lot and speaking with envy of their lord. They'd recall the castle in the days of William Fitz Norman, grandfather of that accursed Hugh who allowed me to be born. Fitz Norman's march into Herefordshire was legendary for he knew that as kinsman of the Conqueror he would be granted what land he wanted. That land included Chipete in Irchenfield, later known as Kilpeck. The English occupant of the castle, the unfortunate Cadiand, was speedily dispossessed.

'This is the seat of William, son of Norman,' declared the upstart, and forthwith gave orders for it to be rebuilt in Norman style.

Now just look at it: cold and forsaken, Norman glory reduced to two jagged walls. So wide is the space between them that the Black Mountains have been magiced into it. Norman supremacy swamped by purple clover.

'Beware the Beast that Bites!' I scream at the visitors, but I cannot bite and they are deaf or am I dumb? I do not understand myself. Desperately I grapple for my identity. Why am I muzzled? A bear's head is feeble. My strength lies in my limbs and loins. Am I to be denied the means to lick my pup? I produce a formless

foetus, only by licking my unformed creation can I arrange it into proper arms and legs.

Surely it is I who am the sculptor and not he who made me? My tongue can lick a living lump into shape and out of chaos I can create a bear whelp. My creator can only work in stone not animated flesh and in jealousy he has tied my mouth. I can neither eat ants to make me well, nor honey to satiate my appetite.

Unborn, unrealised, I am lost in the turbulent cycles of time—neither Celt, Saxon, Viking nor Norman. Am I a monstrous hybrid idol demanding sacrifice? The churchyard wails in protest. The spirits of the monks who dwelt at the priory when this church was built countenanced my creation. Christian dust is seven centuries old hereabouts. Am I then a saint in monstrous garb—like St. Vitus with his four heads? Alas, I am neither pagan nor Christian, for I have no soul. I am exiled from death.

I am lonely but not alone in torment for there are others here with me. See the lovers in frozen embrace! Their lips cannot meet, nor their love be consummated. Even that whore, that sheila-na-gig, has a vagina of stone. She has never sold her body though she presumes to warn young brides entering the church. The fiercesome warrior is doomed to spend eternity with his slain foe, the snake to provide a never-ending feast for birds, the rabbit to forever fear the little dog with the silly face and the falcon to forever feed on its prey.

The Hunt is endless—the game forest is still at the mercy of the Norman Lords of Kilpeck, the keepers of the Haye of Hereford, for they have imposed it on the corbel table here at Kilpeck.

I am here and here I must remain. A muzzled bear cast in stone, incarcerated in a world without end.

Merewald of Kingsland

ead spills from my golden goblet and the drinking horns of my loyal thanes. They hail me as Merewald, Prince of Mercia, son of great Penda. My queen wears a necklace of gold beads, gold bracelets adorn my three beautiful daughters, Milburga, Mildred and Mildgith. Tonight we shall feast on ten geese, five salmon and twenty hens. A pig is still roasting on the fire in the centre of my hall which is hung with tapestries embroidered by my women. My harpist plucks the strings of his lyre and my minstrel sings of battles and heroes. Why then am I sad?

Is it because I can't trust my brothers Peoda and Wolpher who rule over other parts of the kingdom? Or am I still mourning my sons Ethelred and Ethelbright bloodily murdered by their own uncle? No, for blood-feuds and steamy war are a part of our everyday life.

Is it because pestilence killed my infant son Meresin—before we could even open the Leech Book to find a remedy? No, for our infants are always dying from weakness and infection and Mervin at least has survived. Even as I speak, he leaves the feast to release his hawk in the copse.

I am Merewald the Mighty and this is my castle. I have named the place Kingslene, for 'lene' means the land of rivers and 'king' speaks for me, the king—who is sad. My teeth sink into the succulent gooseflesh and as I tear at it, I know why I am sad.

I hear myself shout above the noise of the feast. 'Oh Mighty Woden, oh Tiw, god of war, oh Thor, god of thunder, save me from the black dogs! Every night in my sleep they grab me by the throat. Let me hack them to pieces with my sword instead of that silly old man humiliating great Merewald by removing the dogs with a key.'

My warriors start placating the gods with oaths, believing they are following my example. My minstrel believing his battle song displeases me, sings instead of ferocious monsters who terrorise the Black Mountains.

There is only one who understands, Ceofric, a gentle knight who has lately become what is known as a Christian. 'The good monk Edfride will explain your dream,' he whispers in my ear, 'I found him by the roadside yesterday exhausted by his long walk from Northumbria. I couldn't believe my eyes my lord, he was feeding a fierce lion with bread from his wallet and the beast was actually licking him in gratitude! I tell you, lord, the one God he worships is greater than all these idols put together.'

The boar's head is placed on the table. It has the glazed eyes of an idol challenging me to forsake the old gods. The pork is crisp and our bellies swell with feasting.

Edfride the monk has no belly. His shabby robe hangs on his skeletal frame, his face is haggard and pale yet the joy in his eyes lights up our sombre transitory world.

'I have come to tame a lion,' he announces. His voice is deep and strong in comparison to his body.

'There's no lion here,' I retort looking round quickly in case one appears from nowhere.

'The lion is a fierce pagan called Merewald. I will make him mild and forbearing.' He deserves to have his tongue cut out for that—but I will tell him my dream first.

He listens then explains. 'The black dogs that have you by the throat are Misbelief and Sin and St. Peter is the old man who used his key to Heaven to rescue you from them. They will go on vexing you until you embrace Christ's faith and be converted. Believe in Christ, God's own son who took flesh on him and died for you on a tree. Then you will live forever.'

Live forever? It's too good a chance to miss. I'll become a Christian at once. No more need I regret life's passing, and live in fear of death from famine, plague or the heat of battle.

I am Merewald and I will live forever. The monks can write my story down. It shall be called *The Coming of Edfride*. Kingslene shall be known as King's Leon after my lion to lamb conversion.

Gladly will I give treasure to found a monastery for religious virgins. I'll call it the Religious House of the Lion, or Leominster for short. Edfride is very glad to hear it. There will be no limit to the monasteries I shall found and the glow I feel inside is reflected in the eyes of my most beautiful daughter, Milburga. She is the one destined to marry that oafish Saxon prince who sits ogling her over his platter of salmon. Theirs shall be the first Christian marriage in my kingdom in this year of Our Lord 660.

She rises and kneels before me. She breathes heavily with emotion. Has that princely oaf been in her bower already—is she with child? What is she doing casting off her royal robe and prostrating herself before me?

'Dear Father', she murmurs, 'I beg you, grant my request.'

'Whatever you wish, my dear,' I say. Oh rash paternal love!

'Give me a nunnery, father, so that I can be an abbess. I want to take the veil and become a saint.'

Her lover chokes on a fish bone. Her two sisters rise with one accord and ask for nunneries too. My wife Eormenburga won't be left out; she will establish her own abbey in memory of our sons murdered by that bastard, their own uncle Thunor.

Edfride blesses us for our bounty but insists I forgive Thunor! Forgive that bastard? How many nunneries do I have to build to earn the privilege of cursing him? Treasure-giving is easy, enemy-loving is not.

'Edfride, find me an interpreter, a "Valchstod", to help me negotiate with those Welsh barbarians. We are a violent people in a violent world, we can't beat our swords into ploughshares because you say so. Merewald is no coward but a brave warrior.' At that my noble retainers shout agreement and boast their loyalty to me as is customary at our feasts.

Edfride smiles. 'God give you strength to fight your enemies, but the Church will expect a share of the spoils.' I am satisfied.

The feast is over but the mead still flows. The benches are cleared away; the mats laid out for sleep. Edfride has withdrawn to pray. Moonlight seeps through the tapestry that hangs over the doorway. It sneaks across the floor transforming the fire's embers into red stars. Sleep distorts the image and now the red stars blur into a bloodshot mist.

I strain my eyes to penetrate the glowing gloom. A bloody battle is about to take place to the north of Kingsland. Edward Mortimer, Earl of March, is preparing to fight the Lancastrians at Mortimer's Cross. His soldiers are crying out with fear at the ominous sight of three suns in the sky. My voice reaches Edward across the centuries. 'The spirit of Merewald will not fail you, Edward. Tell them that the three suns represent the Father, Son and Holy Ghost. In the name of God go against your enemies. Be of good heart, trust in God and you'll become king of all England—but don't forget to give the Church a share of the spoils. Build a little chapel on the front of Kingsland Church where folk can pray for the souls of all slain at Mortimer's Cross.'

The souls of the fallen in every Christian battle will live forever but our bodies must die. I will be buried beneath my castle and though my castle will fall, as will that of the Norman impostor who will follow me, the mound will remain and beneath it is Merewald.

Walk along the footpath through the glebe land, west of the church and you will hear the wind in the trees that stand on my grave. Listen—is that the voice of Merewald, who lives forever?

Lady Hawkins of Kington

irgin Queen? Don't you believe it! We ladies of the bedchamber knew different. It was our secret: that once our Virgin Queen had passed the age of child-bearing, her favourites became her lovers.

But, poor soul, she'd only reveal what was necessary. Far better to keep a ruff over her dewlap, pull an auburn wig over her bald pate and let jewels distract a darling's eye from her creased skin.

'Smooth away my wrinkles with arsenic powder, Mistress Vaughan,' she'd say. My loyalty would battle with resentment, for we had to prepare her body for love-making whereas she insisted on us remaining unmarried. It was worse for me; I wasn't pretty so men looked elsewhere. Spinsterhood became an increasingly hard price to pay for a place at her glittering Court.

And how glittering it once seemed to a girl brought up in remote Kington where the hills melt into the distance of the Welsh mountains. We enjoyed prestige locally, my father Charles Vaughan was M.P. for Radnor and we lived in the big timbered house known as Hergest Court.

My mother was proud of being part of an important border family. I was her namesake, Margaret, her favourite child out of the eight. Her life was confinement after confinement; for me she wanted more. That I should be summoned from remote Herefordshire to serve Her Majesty was the answer to her prayers. And of course I was keen. Romance and adventure lay in wait, not forgetting gossip and scandal! We had heard about the gallantry of Sir Ambrose Cave who had bought the town of Kington off the queen in 1564. When her garter slipped off at a dance, the saucy fellow picked it up and offered to put it on for her. When she refused, he tied it on his arm and vowed to wear it for the rest of his life. He did too, for when he rode into Kington her garter was still on his arm.

A golden future beckoned. I wanted to escape my mother's fate for I had heard her screams when my sisters and younger brother were born. It was different for the boys—my eldest brother William led a thrilling life sailing to the Spanish Main with John Hawkins from Devon.

It was William that made Sir John seek me out years later at Court. He was no longer the dashing young seadog that I had once briefly known but he still had charisma and I was flattered by his attention. His expeditions had earnt him the reputation of a gruff, hard-bitten fighter and ruthless slave trader. Yet there was no ruthlessness in the eyes of the desperate Admiral who had come to plead for thousands of his sailors who were dying from dysentery after saving England from the Armada.

'The streets of Margate, Deal and Dover are awash with disease, Mistress Margaret. I beg you, intercede with Her Majesty. Surely she can spare some gold from her coffers to build a hospital for her English heroes?'

It was so sad. John's young cousin Francis Drake was now the apple of her eye, the acknowledged hero who had defeated the Armada. But we'd have had a Spaniard on the throne today if John Hawkins hadn't changed the design of our ships. It was our fast little ships that beat those gluttonous Spanish tubs!

Anyway, he obtained his hospital and a wife into the bargain. A royal suggestion is a royal command and I was pleased to settle for an aging husband who couldn't forget his first wife and her recent lingering death. I was plain, so what more could I expect? At least I could still bear children, God willing, and I prayed that he would give me a child, for his only son by Dame Katherine had turned out ill—I had often heard it said at Court that Richard Hawkins was unworthy to be a captain in Her Majesty's fleet.

John and I were married in 1592 and moved into our new home, The Dolphin, in Tower Street, London. All I wanted was to give him children, ironically that was never to be. On our wedding night I lay in our four-poster listening to his snoring, wondering if he were capable of fathering a child—he was sixty after all. Or was it my fault—had I disappointed him? I suppose I always knew it was the queen he really loved even more than his first wife. Our Virgin Queen used me to satisfy his diminishing carnal urges while she dallied with her young gallants and kept my husband's undying affection.

We were married for three years but only spent a few weeks together. Indeed, the marriage was barely consummated before he was off to sea on secret commissions for the queen. In 1595 he sailed for the Caribbean, never to return. It was a double tragedy for me as my brother William was also killed at Porto Rico. Even on his deathbed John's last thoughts were not of me, but of Her. Poor soul, he wanted to recompense her for her losses on his expedition and left her £2,000—as if She cared!

My world crumbled. I mourned for a love that might have been but never was—it was all I had. They brought his body home and I buried him at St. Dunstan's in the East. Now all I wanted was to go home, to escape from misplaced expressions of sympathy and the sidelong glances of those who knew the truth, to faraway Kington. Many years had passed since I had left.

It was a hard journey. We met drovers bringing Welsh cattle and sheep to London and they warned us of floods ahead. Ruts in the mud tracks that served as roads became deeper still and finally I had to abandon my carriage and continue on horseback, assisted by my faithful steward and my reluctant maid. I didn't care, I was glad of the rain on my face and the mud soaking into my shoes, for it took the mind off the painful memories I was determined to leave behind. We were forced to cut across fields in the driving rain, for fear of being drowned in the roads.

I had forgotten how wild this country can be. At last we crossed the little bridge over the River Arrow—we had reached Kington, but relief turned to disappointment. The houses in Bridge Street huddled together as though they were suspicious of this stranger who had come out of the mist. I was no stranger to the innkeeper at The Talbot, however. He welcomed us so warmly I hardly noticed his uncouth manner. His ale was invigorating, and he insisted on stabling our horses and gave us his carriage and horses for the remaining two miles of the journey.

So, in our landlord's leaking carriage, I was bumped up Castle Hill where there is no castle. Kington has never needed a proper castle to keep out Welsh invaders because our culture is partly Welsh. That ignorant upstart Offa actually placed Kington in Wales when he put his dyke two miles east of the town. Our castle, such as it was, seems to have been a watchtower on the church mound and by 1230 even that had been abandoned.

In the church is the tomb of my notorious ancestor: Sir Thomas Vaughan. He's known as Black Vaughan, the bad spirit of Kington. 'What did he do wrong?' I dared to ask my father—the subject was taboo in our family.

'He was killed at the Battle of Banbury and he was a Yorkist.' He spat back, as if that explained everything.

I had a nightmare about Black Vaughan, bloody in his black armour. Paralysed with fear, I'd watch him remove his helmet as slowly, agonisingly slowly, a bull's head came out. It lowered its horns and charged—and I'd awake screaming with terror.

The fact is we're all terrified of him round here and people actually kept away from Kington market for fear of meeting him. He was said to have appeared first as a bluebottle fly, but the evil force was so strong he turned into a Hereford bull and went into the church.

Exorcism was tried of course. Twelve parsons with candles in the presence of a new-born babe tried to read the tormented spirit into a silver snuff-box. It must have been terrifying. The spirit materialised, yelling out, 'I was fierce when I was a man, but fiercer now, for I am a devil.' All the parsons were powerless except one who reduced the spirit to the size of the bluebottle fly and caught it in the snuff box.

I told myself there was nothing to fear as I entered the church to give thanks for my safe arrival, after all the snuff box is supposed to be buried at the bottom of our pool at Hergest for a thousand years. I have a strange premonition that he will begin to stir as the year 2000 approaches: some men will be clearing the pool of silt when a fierce burst of bubbles from its depths will stop them working for fear of Black Vaughan.

His wife, Ellen the Terrible, who was buried beside him, was reputed to have attended an archery tournament dressed as a man and shot her brother's murderer. I know how she felt; I could have murdered the Spanish devils who killed my brother William in Porto Rico.

Don't gain the wrong impression: we Vaughans had an illustrious pedigree. We were much admired locally for encouraging the arts and learning through the centuries.

Oh God, how would I cope with the illiterate people along the border? Even the lad who turned the spit in the royal kitchen could sign his name. Yet when I was a girl, I remember how I'd listen enraptured to Welsh bards who had never held a pen. I would have to do what I could to help these people, and as John had left me a rich woman I would found a school so that all the children of Kington could learn to read and write. The pupils could attend church every Sunday and give an account of the sermon on Monday morning in my school—the Lady Hawkins school.

It's time the Kington folk came out of the Dark Ages. Can you credit it: they actually believed that the enormous rock called the Whetstone goes down from the summit of Hergest Ridge to drink in the Hindwell Brook as soon as it hears the cock crow! It's as though our Celtic heritage has swept down from the mountains to envelop us in superstition. As we turned down the lonely Hergest road and left Kington behind us, I prayed I would not fall 'under the evil tongue' of a witch. Even at Court they believed in witches, and the Queen's heir, James of Scotland, was said to be writing a book about them. In this wild and desolate place it was easy to believe witches existed. But if I was apprehensive, my maid was terrified.

Born and bred in Cheapside this journey was a nightmare for her. I tried to raise her spirits by encouraging her to look forward to the six fairs we had in Kington from February to October.

'Why so many, madam?' she asked bravely as a flash of lightning lit up Hergest Court, ivy brushing beardlike over its mournful black and white face. Not the moment to tell her that the servants' quarters on the top floor were haunted by a demon dog: The Hound of the Vaughans!

Instead I regaled her with tales of greedy Sir Ambrose Cave, the Lord of the Manor who promoted the fairs and markets because he was paid a toll for all the livestock sold on fair and market days. He didn't care if brutal fights broke out because some farmers understandably disputed his right to collect the tolls.

As we climbed out of the carriage, the front door of the court was opened and my world was suddenly transformed. I was in the arms of my younger brother Charles, while my nieces Margaret and Elizabeth pulled eagerly at my wet cloak in anticipation of my embrace. Friendly flames licked the logs in the grate, flinging a warm glow round the hall.

I had left behind the world of sycophants and courtly favour, I had come home to my family's hearth.

Katherine Audley of Ledbury

I was thirty-three and I wanted my life back. It had never really been my own, for I had belonged first to my father and then to my husband.

I was the first child of a turbulent union. My mother, Matilda, Countess of Salisbury, was the widow of William Longspée the Younger and had had other daughters by that marriage. She didn't want to marry my father, Sir John Giffard, though they say he was a dashing and courageous soldier, so he took her by force from her manor house at Canford, near Wimborne in Dorset, to his castle at Brimpsfield and held her there against her will. But in those days my mother wasn't submissive and sent secret letters of complaint to King Henry III who called Sir John into his presence. My father hotly denied that he had kidnapped her and promptly offered the king 300 marks because he had married without the royal licence. This was accepted on condition that my mother made no further complaint. Believing herself pregnant, she was in no position to object and the marriage was declared legal in March 1271, shortly before my mother miscarried. I was born the following year. They named me Katherine after the saint of Alexandria because I was born on her day.

My mother never lived to see me married. She lived in sad, resentful submission to my father, giving him two more daughters but no sons. The love of her life had been William, her first husband and she died with his name on her lips.

Father quickly married again, but poor Alicia Maltravers also died—within days of their wedding. Scarcely was Alicia in her grave than father married Margaret Neville. What an appetite he had for wives! He had tired of delicate beauties and Margaret was a fierce giant of a woman. Father soon realised what he had taken on—for she dominated him as she also dominated our household with her rasping voice and commanding presence. 'I'll outlive him and he'll give me a son,' she declared vehemently, and she was right. My younger sisters endured her, but I could not. I complied with my father's wish that I should marry, but I cared not whom, for I was convinced that no man could be as dreadful as Margaret Neville.

Nicholas Audley was a Marcher Lord, responsible for keeping order along the Welsh border. I was fifteen and he was nearly thirty, but kind and comfortingly paternal and, according to father, 'a suitable match.' My marriage almost coincided with the birth of my step-brother and within the year I was pregnant myself. I wanted a daughter—someone to love and share my feelings. My mother had borne me unwillingly and had died when I needed her most. My daughter would be loved and cherished. Yet, during the pangs of labour, I had a vision of my mother, with hair of burnished gold. I begged her to take me to her, but she shook her head and her tears soaked my face. 'I am so weary, mother,' I pleaded. 'I am with William and at peace,' she replied, 'and you, child, will find rest where bells ring of their own accord. That will be your sign.' I strained to hear more, but pain overcame me and I slipped into unconsciousness.

I was delivered—of a boy, Thomas. The church bells rang in celebration and reminded me of my mother's strange prophecy. I

was never to forget it. The birth of Nicholas followed two years later, and then, praise God, my daughter Ela was born. This was just before my husband left with horse and arms to join King Edward I who was planning to reconquer Gascony. He was away from home a lot on various campaigns for the king after Ela's birth, and unable to forbid my dismissal of the wet nurse so that I might breast-feed my own daughter. Ela hardly saw her father. In 1298, he rode out with his three knights and twelve men to join the king who was gathering an enormous army to invade Scotland and avenge William Wallace's victory at Stirling Bridge.

The following year two of those knights brought my husband's body home. They said he had distinguished himself bravely at the battle of Falkirk and the king was grateful. It was so unreal. Tom, only ten, immediately tried to assume his father's role in the house and bullied eight year old Nick. Our reeve fussed around, lamenting not only his lord's death, but the lack of fat on his geese which would be required for the wake. Only six year old Ela wept with me. We had both, it seemed, lost a father whom neither of us hardly knew. Perhaps God reproached me for the way I regarded my husband, for in that same year He took my own father too.

Suddenly I found myself a widow with three children of tender age—and an orphan into the bargain.

However, my father's death brought me considerable material security at a time when the king gave the wardship of my husband's lands to Count Amadeus of Savoy whilst Tom was a minor. From father I inherited the castle and town of Llandovery for which I was required to do homage to King Edward. In addition I received land held by my husband in Shropshire, Staffordshire and Cheshire. From his deeds, I discovered that I owned a fishpond, sundry mills, woodland and an iron-mine.

Financially I was secure but disorientated with no paternal figure to command me. I knew, however, that I had no desire to be wooed again—to belong to another man. Although I was a woman, I had, I told myself, more influence in my world than many a man of lesser rank or smaller possessions. And I had Ela, my other self, with my deep brown eyes and braided chestnut hair. What delight I took in watching her grow and listening to her play to me; her supple fingers moving over the strings of the lyre while her music flowed into my soul. I knew I must not be selfish. Many girls were married at twelve, I was myself a bride at fifteen: some weddings were even solemnized in the cradle. Ela was beautiful and her dowry considerable: a good husband must be found for her. I was worried lest she be left alone in the world, a feeling reinforced by the sudden death of my elder son Tom, in 1307, a shock from which I was sure I would never recover. He was only eighteen and had fallen sick and died whilst campaigning with the old king. His wardship passed into the hands of the new King Edward who granted it to Piers Gaveston, for Nicholas was still a minor.

Ela must marry, but whom? She must have some say in the matter herself; she must be happy. I would sit by the narrow window in the solar, embroidering tapestry, smelling the sweet earth wet from the rain that rose from my little garden below, imagining the husband for Ela. I must make the effort to accompany her to the Court for I was, after all, a cousin of the king. Surely she would have the opportunity of meeting suitable suitors there.

How things had changed at Court since the days of the old king, and not for the better. Piers Gaveston, the new king's close friend, was so insufferably arrogant; courtiers flocked round him to gain the king's favour. Only one stood apart: his name was James de Perers. Any man brave enough to ignore Gaveston was worthy of my daughter. Perhaps he sensed my admiration; his eyes met mine and held my glance for a minute that seemed like an hour. In that moment of time, his face was etched on my memory forever. Ridiculous, he was at least ten years younger than I, and a widow in her mid-thirties had no right to be attracted to a daughter's potential suitor. And suitor he became, as though he read my mind. With a pleasure that was bittersweet, I watched him kiss Ela's hand and lead her out to dance, after the king, amidst much merriment, had taken the floor with Gaveston.

One evening a few weeks later, while in my manor house on my dower lands in Shropshire, I became aware of Ela standing behind me, watching me unbraid my hair which fell to the floor in chestnut waves now streaked with silver. 'Mother dear,' she murmured, moving to kiss my cheek, 'you know how you have always wanted me to choose my own husband ...'

I held my breath, waiting for the name of James de Perers to fall from her lips. I both longed and dreaded to hear it.

'I want to marry Griffin de la Pole.'

Who was he? Then I remembered him—a pale thin fair boy with a cultivated laugh like Gaveston's. I was horrified but her happiness was all important to me and they were soon married. She was just sixteen and I prayed she wouldn't regret her choice. I would never return to Court for I determined never to see James de Perers again: never to meet his gaze again across a crowded hall. How could she have rejected him?

Save for my servants, I was alone now in my castle at Llandovery. I had lost my parents, my husband and my first born son, my younger son had grown into busy manhood, and now my cherished daughter had married. I was beholden to no-one. I was thirty-five and I had got my life back but I didn't know what to do with it. I missed Ela desperately and I tried not to think about James. It was time to put the past behind me and be at peace with myself. I needed a complete change of surroundings, where there were no memories. Then I remembered that my husband's half-brother, Hugh de Audley, held the estate of Haskyll, part of the manor in Ledbury in Herefordshire. I determined to go there: to make a new start in a new place. I would take only a few servants: my trusty steward William and my devoted maid, Mabel, among them.

It was a long way from Llandovery to Ledbury. I travelled in a horse-litter whose curtains protected me from the cold winds of early April. My servants followed with the packhorses. We stopped at monasteries overnight, where I showed my gratitude for hospitality by giving alms, for the good monks not only look after travellers but also collect money for the repair of local roads and bridges, very necessary in that wild country through which we journeyed until we reached the walled city of Hereford. Here, by kind invitation of Bishop Richard Swinfield, I lodged in the Bishop's Palace before continuing the journey to Ledbury the next day.

As we entered the town we crossed a water-splash at the crossroads and came to a sudden halt. There was a terrible noise of squealing pigs and I realised, with horror, that this was where the butchers slaughtered their animals so that the water could wash the blood away. We were indeed caught up in the hurlyburly of the market place which was wedge-shaped like the one in Hereford, and full of pigs, cattle, sheep and poultry. Surrounded by butchers' stalls and the acrid stench of recent slaughter, there was no way our horses could pass through. To make matters worse, a cheeky pedlar thrust his florid face into mine in an effort to sell me his trinkets. That decided me. I would have to dismount from the litter and continue on foot. So my steward William pushed through the crowds and animals to make way for me and my maid, past stalls that seemed to grow out of the very houses. Was everyone shouting, 'What d'ye lack? What d'ye lack?' at me? Jostled by folk and livestock alike, what I certainly lacked was peace and quiet. For all that, I was glad to see the saddlers, spurriers and farriers doing a good trade, for my grooms needed their services. And in spite of myself, I paused at the garlanders' stall, to Mabel's delight, who was also tempted by the dazzling circlets of gold and silver.

'Keep hold of your purse strings my lady,' warned William, 'there be pickpockets about.'

'That must be the church down there, William,' I replied, noticing the tower in the distance. 'We'll take that lane, it'll be quieter there, and I want to give thanks for our safe arrival.'

It was more like a cathedral than a church, with a detached tower that had been newly built to replace the crossing-tower. Inside, space merged with the delicate beauty of the tracery on the windows, the intricate circles of the window on the north aisle and the slender rolls barring the west window. This was another world—such a contrast from the hub-bub of the market outside.

As I knelt to pray, I became aware that I was speaking to God on my own behalf, I wasn't praying, as was my custom, for the souls of my father, husband and son—not even for the happiness of my daughter. I prayed to 'my' father not 'our' father, drifting on a silent sea from the family shore to which I had been tethered so long. That shore was fading and I was adrift—going I knew not where, but I was no longer afraid. I had a new sense of self, as though I were another Katherine.

Whilst I was in the church, William had arranged for the horses to be brought to the church door and I was soon riding on a pillion seat behind a servant, back down the High Street which was dominated by a red stone and timbered building with three lancet windows in its eastern end. Another church? A monastery perhaps? No, it was a hospital: St. Katherine's, my namesake. It couldn't be coincidence. William must wait with the horses while I went inside, accompanied by a reluctant Mabel.

Inside was one great open hall, which housed the beds of the inmates along the north and south walls and also served as a chapel. 'Angel of Mercy, some ale I beg you!' called an old man from his bed. 'Don't touch him, my lady,' breathed Mabel, but I took his wrinkled hand, wincing at the touch of the ulcerous flesh, while one of the brethren raised the fellow to a sitting position so that I could press the cup of ale to his lips.

From the monk I learnt about the place—it had been founded by Hugh Foliot in 1232 'to the honour of the Lord and of St. Katherine the Virgin as a constant reminder to all in the market place of the need for prayer and works of charity.'

'The bishop's palace used to be here, my lady,' he continued, 'but as the town grew, so did the noise and the smells. The bishop also objected to the intrusion on his privacy, so he moved out of town, leaving all his barns, malt houses, cider houses and the like empty. About a third of the market place it was and so the land became available for our hospital—and it's well used as you see, my lady.'

'I can see,' I assured him. 'And if you will allow me to visit your inmates again and bring them some comfort, I will, gladly.'

'May God bless you, my lady,' he replied.

The brethren welcomed my interest and invited me to stay for Mass which the Chaplain was about to celebrate. As I listened to the intercessionary prayers, I was warmed by words that alleviated the terrible fear of divine punishment. Expressions on puckered faces softened and a sense of everlasting mercy filled the hospital.

I would have stayed longer had not William appeared, to Mabel's relief, to remind me that it was getting late and, though Haskyll Manor was only just outside the town, we must be there before dark.

Indeed, Bailiff Hunte and his wife Agnes were waiting at the manor to greet me. As I warmed myself beside the wood fire burning in the hall, I attributed my late arrival to my visit to St.

Katherine's Hospital. 'So, where's the bishop's palace, then?' I asked Agnes, who clearly had been waiting to regale me with her local knowledge.

'Beyond Upper Cross now, my lady. You couldn't really blame him moving, could you, not when he spends his life travelling between his manor houses—all twenty-four of them. And Ledbury is his favourite after all, specially when he's got royal visitors.' She lowered her voice out of respect and added confidentially, 'much better than at Hereford, his palace there's more like a court than a

home, and it's in the city. The new palace at Upper Cross has so much park and chase with it, stretching right to the top of the Malverns. Do ye remember the last time Bishop Swinfield came to Ledbury, Thomas?' Her husband nodded; he knew it was useless to interrupt. 'You've never seen the like, my lady—the procession never ended, he rode with his squires and forty attendants at the head. Then came his valets, clerk of the chapel, chief carter, larderer, porter, stable groom, butler, chamberlain, farrier, head huntsman, messenger and falconer.' Was she out of breath at last? Evidently not, just searching her memory to ensure she left no-one out. 'And they weren't all, my lady, there were the kitchen servants, the cook, baker, undergroom and such folk as pageboys and them that work in the bakehouse, stables and kennels. You should have seen the packhorses, my lady, with the furniture and the draught horses pulling the chamber and kitchen carts—God help us, our carts still get stuck in the ruts it all made in our roads.'

According to Agnes, I would soon have the pleasure of dining with Bishop Swinfield, whose hospitality I had already enjoyed in his absence the previous night at Hereford. 'Do you know, my lady, when he kept open house for his tenants and friends last Easter, there was so much food I couldn't believe my eyes—'twere one carcass of salt beef and one of fresh, 5 pigs, 4 and a half calves, 22 kids, 3 fat deer, 12 capons, 88 pigeons and nearly 2,000 eggs. My husband took account so I know exactly what was there, my lady, and 60 gallons of wine ....'

At that moment the valiant Thomas interrupted swiftly to explain that in daylight I would be able to see the vineyards from Haskyll Manor, stretching across the Wall Hills, but that now I must be thirsty and hungry myself after my journey, so he and his wife would leave me to dine and retire in peace.

That night I lay in the big wooden bed with its feather mattress, bolster, linen sheets and a coverlet of fur, too exhausted to sleep. I thought about Katherine the saint, after whom the hospital was named. I focused on the room around me, on the pole sticking out from the wall on which my clothes were hung. In the candlelight it looked like the spoke of a gigantic wheel.

Sleep when it came was fitful: why was I shouting, 'I am a bride of Christ; don't persecute me?' but they took no notice. Where were they taking me? An enormous wheel loomed out of the mist. They were tying me to it, the rope cut into my wrists. I saw a face over the heads of my persecutors: it was the old man whose hand I had held that day and he was praying for me. The wheel was turning, slowly tearing my limbs; I must bear the pain as Christ bore the cross. 'God forgive you!' I shouted at the leering faces of my torturers and the wheel shattered throwing me clear. I woke as I fell, bathed in sweat but strangely refreshed and relieved to be at home, for it felt like home even though I had been in Ledbury less than a day.

And so I settled to a new routine, supervising Bailiff Hunte in the management of my brother-in-law's estate, for I had become skilled in the niceties of tenure and feudal law while my husband had been away serving his king. Then there was the practical side: overseeing the making of butter and cheese, the baking of bread from the corn grown on the manor and the brewing of ale. I had to lay in a good supply of salt to fill the great salting tubs in the larder where bacon was cured, candles made and winter meat salted down. I reassessed my personal income too, allocating more to almsgiving to benefit St. Katherine's Hospital and reducing my expenditure on jewels and gowns. The encumbrances of the world were becoming increasingly unimportant to me. I didn't wish to entertain or be entertained, only to visit the Hospital to comfort the poor and the sick. I was happy in Ledbury; I was here to stay, or so I thought before Ela's messenger arrived with that first letter.

It told of the untimely death of her young husband, Griffin. I was not to grieve and not to travel for it was December. 'Of course, I must go,' I said to myself, 'she needs me.'

Evidently she didn't, for scarcely had I made arrangements for my journey, than another messenger arrived with her second letter. Within days of Griffin's death, she had married another: James de Perers! They had been fined for marrying without a licence. Was she carrying his child? A wave of nausea swept over me, but it was their affair—not mine and they were miles away. Then I read the rest of her letter. 'The bishop of Hereford has offered us a house at Ledbury, dear Mother, with land and property. We shall be moving there in the spring, to be near you. James sends you his love. Your loving daughter, Ela.'

I was ashamed of myself: I didn't want them in Ledbury; I had left that old life behind. I was different now, a different Katherine. There was nothing for it; I would have to move on—wander till I found another sanctuary. But I knew they'd follow me. I felt a mixture of shame, anger and frustration and there was only one way to overcome these feelings.

'I must to church,' I told Mabel who, startled by the harsh tone in a voice that was always gentle, hurriedly brought my cloak.

'We must wander further Mabel,' I told her as we walked the mile to the church.

'Leave Ledbury, my lady? But you are so happy here.'

'I must find peace, Mabel,' I shouted above the howling, bitterly cold wind. The track led across a frozen field: we crouched for a moment in the shelter of a rock which lay beside the path. I was exhausted more from the turmoil within me than from the elements without.

The wind ceased: the world was eerily silent, as if it held its breath in expectation, then trembled with excitement as the music began. Heavenly bells were ringing, melting the echoing hills with sweet tones that they might swell the sound. Who was ringing such bells? With one accord, Mabel and I ran to the church to find out. I watched as she wrestled in vain with the iron handle on the belfry door. 'The belfry is locked, my lady. Merciful God, the belfry is locked! There is no-one here—and them bells are still ringing!'

So they were, the bells were ringing without human hands. I leant against the tower and closed my eyes to listen to the miraculous melody. My mother's face swam into view. 'Here you will set up your rest, Katherine,' she murmured, 'that is God's will.'

Set up my rest? What did God mean? He answered with a mighty crack of thunder and a flash of lightning lit up the church wall to show me a small house built against it. My cell. I was to become a recluse. I told the bishop and he agreed that such a cell should be built on consecrated ground where I could see and share the offices of the Church. (He couldn't really refuse, for after all I was a cousin of the king). As a recluse, I would be as one dead with no daughter, nor even son-in-law to intrude on my peace.

And so it happened. By the time James and Ela arrived in Ledbury, my cell was ready, thanks to the good offices of

Ledbury's priest, John de Almeley, and the blessing of his bishop who gave me the last rites as though I were dying. How strange to hear my own burial service read!

The door was locked: I was never again to leave my cell. Dear Mabel alone was allowed to attend me, at her own wish—for women recluses are permitted a servant to procure food, firewood and other necessaries. Mabel intercepted calls at the little window—so I heard James's voice, and Ela's too, but I never spoke to either again and they stopped coming, leaving me to only the muted voice of worship rising from the congregation of a thousand or more. I had all I wanted in this life. The king gave me a royal pension of £30 a year, granted tó 'the recluse of Ledbury' as I became known. I relinquished all my property in favour of my son, Nicholas, receiving only an annuity of £100 for myself. On Christmas Day and at Easter, the bishop sent me cheese, eggs and fruit. He was my spiritual director and bade me never be idle, to speak little, pray, study and meditate, observe the daily offices and work with my hands. I had a loom and spun sheep's wool into thread and wove it into rough cloth, for my clothes must be simple, warm and well-kept.

I was, of course, tempted as are all solitaries. It was especially hard for a high-born lady to live like a peasant. 'Virtue should flourish in such as leave this world,' the bishop said, but virtue isn't easy. For a while I lusted after James, then exhausted by fervent prayer, all the people I had ever loved: my mother, father, husband, sons, daughter—and son-in-law, merged into one, into a dim yet vivid consciousness of divine love. This love nourished patience, gentleness, kindness and peace. Outside, misrule, lawlessness, plague and pestilence afflicted the world. My son, Nicholas, died in 1316, James de Perers too. Ela married again and during the civil wars plotted against the king, so that my little grandson at only eight years old found himself a hostage in the Tower. All this I knew, but I remained at peace for I had found myself at last.

Jenny Pipes of Leominster

e grateful, Jenny my girl, be grateful!' my old mother would say. Be grateful that I was one of the last of the poor children to attend the charity school over the old engine-house where the fire engines lived.

'Jenny can read!' my mother boasted.

'Won't do her any good,' my father retorted, 'our Jenny must know her place.'

By God, I know my place alright—but how I'd love to have gone to one of those so-called respectable boarding schools, learnt French and dancing so that I could wear a fashionable gown and attend the Dancing Assemblies held in Leominster every winter at the King's Arms in Corn Street. I'd look with such disdain on the lads hiring out the post-chaises and horses outside as I swept past into the glowing ballroom. But that's not for Jenny Pipes. No liveried servant from the King's Arms would be seen dead with me.

'Be grateful, Jenny my girl, be grateful!' Mother prattles on and no doubt will do so for many a year—for we live to a grand old age in Leominster. They say 'tis the two open commons lying on the north and east sides of the town that ventilate the atmosphere by causing air to circulate rapidly and disperse germs.

True, we seldom have epidemics, though of course we fear the smallpox. The rich have been inoculated, but many of us poorer folk are still unprotected in spite of assurances from patronising physicians.

Take my husband (and you're welcome to the wretch), he needs a doctor. I swear he's suffering from canine madness after being bitten by that fierce hound, for he does nothing but rant at me when he's not snoring in drunken slumber. 'Get off your butt!' I say, 'and earn yourself one shilling and eight pence a day with beer, for mowing grass! If you can't get that job, at least earn one shilling and sixpence a day with beer for mowing lawns.' The beer might get him there! God, how I rue the day I swore to love, honour and obey John Corran. He can't even support himself, let alone a wife. If it hadn't been for my spinning, I swear I'd have ended up in the Union Workhouse at the Old Priory, where those mean overseers administer the Poor Rate.

I'm damned if I'll be brought that low. It's bad enough being beholden to my brother-in-law, Will the chandler, who lets us share his house with his wife and seven children—he says I'm a bad influence with my loud mouth, but he knows his useless brother has married a good worker. Everyone sees me spinning at the open door on summer days, watching for the water-carrier, who brings fresh water round in a barrel, selling it at a halfpenny a bucket. 'Only two buckets, Jenny,' my honest brother-in-law reminds me, 'that's all you're allowed!' The sun warms my face as I spin, but Lud, how this town stinks! Hardly surprising since livestock is sold in our streets. We live in New Street, where the stench is worse after the sheep and pig market moved here two years ago. It's a damn sight worse in South Street at the horse market, though. Still, old Jenny doesn't miss a trick. Wasn't it my idea to put a pen for animals on the front of the house on Fair days so we could charge for it? Even so, come a wet day and the place is a mire of repulsive filth under-foot; sometimes we even sink knee-deep in it. That's bad enough,

95

but then the leaden water spouts drench us from above. If a cart or waggon isn't bogged down, it'll have got stuck anyway in a street where the very houses are malicious, sticking out to block the way.

'Tis worse at night for glimmering lamps are few and far between. 'We will repair and pave the streets of Leominster!' boast the self-elected Corporation—but at what a price! Those devils mean to enclose our commons and let them out to the rich. Losing Broadward Common, Midsummer and Lammas Meadows and Portna Moor will ruin poor cottagers, for they'll have nowhere to pasture a few sheep and a solitary cow. It's the old story, the bloody rich reap the harvest and the poor go to the wall.

'Twas just the same with the Turnpike Trusts. What poor man can afford to pay for improved roads? We never had to pay before. It's so unfair. Only the rich benefit from Turnpike Tolls, the highest bidder getting the right to collect them from the poor.

It's no good they telling me that the Corporation—for all their grand oaths of office taken in the Court-House in Church Street— are improving the town for us. Those immoral stuck-ups declare modern red-brick houses 'respectable', but what is wrong with our black and white timber and plaster houses with their curious grotesque carvings? They're less expensive to rent—which is why we live in one, all twelve of us and that includes my old mother. Will pays the rent, of course, not John. What's good enough for the Butter-Cross, as we lower class folk call the Townhall, is good enough for us, for hasn't that splendid timber and plaster building lasted nearly 200 years? Many's the time I've stood beneath it, in the open spaces between its twelve oak pillars, where the butter market's held and bought eggs and butter for Will's growing family, not forgetting my prattling old mother and my bastard of a husband.

I hate him. He's no good in bed, but 'tis I who bear the stigma: 'Jenny's barren!' They whisper. 'Take Widow Welch's Pills for female complaints,' advises my sister-in-law Mary as she prepares for her eighth lying-in, ''tis a celebrated tonic, it'll remove all obstructions in your system.' God help me, 'tis obstructions in his system I need to remove. No wonder I went to Betty Hughes, the wonder-worker of Kingsland!

Yes, I know, the gentry say she's a fraud, for how can a mere labourer's wife be a miracle-worker? They've not heard of the carpenter of Nazareth! Post-chaises don't bring wealthy pilgrims from Dover and Portsmouth to visit a fake! 'Make me conceive, Betty!' I begged as yet another cripple threw away his crutches. She touched my womb and uttered a short prayer before whispering, 'Your womb is fruitful, Jenny. A man is what you need. No, I'll not take your money. Go in peace, lass.'

I knew it then for certain—the sod was impotent—but I daren't say so, his brother would turn me and my old mother on to the streets. It'd be the workhouse for us then alright. But what could I do? How could I possibly get Betty to cure John? He would never go to her. I could beg her to come to him. Might he yet give me a child? I would have to hurry for those accursed magistrates wanted Betty out of Herefordshire. They said she was an impostor and they'd imprison her if she didn't 'cease her deceptions'.

But my luck was out. When I returned, John was gone. I was used to him riding off with Tom, an equally undesirable character, in search of taverns new, no doubt. Normally I'd have been grateful but that night I desperately wanted to talk him round. I would pretend, I decided, that his presence at my side would enable Betty to cure my sterility, that way he would never know that he was the one she was curing. Where, in Heaven's name, was he?

Sure enough, by the next morning, a prophet dishonoured in her own county, Betty had left—for Oxford, where we soon heard crowds were witnessing her miracles. John returned, drunk of course, to slump on the bed having flung his hat on the floor. I picked it up; there was a hole in its crown as though a bullet had passed through it.

'My God, what have you been about, John?' I yelled at the inert heap.

'Be off, you nagging woman!' he grunted and grabbed at my arm, twisting it until I thought it would break.

I forgot the hat for during that night my sister-in-law, Mary, went into labour. I attended her throughout her pains—not till the birds started their dawn chorus was she delivered—of her eighth child, a puny boy. She had suffered for nothing, for he would surely die. 'By God,' I cried in exasperation, 'he'll ne'er see the end of the week!'

'Quiet, you blasphemous woman!' ordered Will. But my poor sister-in-law frowning at me through her tears was punishment enough.

I was out of favour, as usual, but it fell to me to feed and care for the rest of the family. They had been promised a visit to Leominster's Rural Sports in honour of His Majesty's 71st birthday on 5 June, 1809. They had been looking forward to it for weeks. But church came first at the Priory. I regret I had to give young Henry a slap round the head for kicking his sister in the middle of Master Williams' sermon. Master Williams .... the only man I respect in this world (and it's nothing to do with his being so hand-some), because he really cares about folk although he's a gentleman and headmaster of the grammar school and curate of the Priory Church.

'How is Mistress Mary and her new baby?' he asks at the church door. 'Will we see you this afternoon, Mistress Corran, in the foot-race for young ladies between 15 and 30?'

'Well, by God, you'll not see me in the one for ladies over 40!' I retort and curse my foul tongue. But the dear man wasn't offended and merely joked, 'I'm sure none of those will be found!'

Did I sweat in that race—twice round Midsummer Common I went with my nieces and nephews cheering me on, and came in first to receive a pound of tea from the hand of Master Williams. I was so overcome I actually managed to thank him without swearing. I quickly made up for it, though, by laughing rudely at a neighbour's fall from the greasy pole and his subsequent failure to win the prized leg of mutton. I was just about to yield to Henry and Matilda's persistent tugging at my skirt because they didn't want to miss the donkey races, when I overheard something to remind me of John's hat.

'A bad business last night on the Shrewsbury road for Squire Clay, weren't it? He's not expected to live. Accosted by two men he were; one tried to seize his bridle but the squire's horse leapt from him, it being a superior steed like and the squire galloped off with the villains firing their pistols after 'im. Tho' he were badly wounded, the squire, being a good shot himself as ye know, whipped out 'is own pistol and fired back—but he were weak from loss of blood and 'e missed the scoundrel and hit 'is 'at. The ball passed right thro' the top, 'is valet said. That halted 'em alright, right cowards they were.'

'Did he know the villains?' I interrupted breathlessly.

The old fellow turned round, pleased to have interested another in his news. 'No indeed, lass; 'twas too dark to see their faces, but one was "rather corpulent" squire said.'

I didn't wait for more. 'We're going home!' I told the complaining children.

Will was at the door. 'Where the hell is John?' I screamed at him.

'Have you no respect, woman,' he scolded, 'the baby is dead.'

I heard without understanding what he was saying. I was obsessed. 'Where the hell is John, the murdering swine! He's a killer!' I screamed as I ran up the stairs. 'His hat has a hole in it!'

Then John was there, grabbing my shoulders and shaking me roughly. 'What rubbish are you talking? I've a new hat, bought it at D'Vall's in West Street this morning.'

'That proves your guilt!' I shrieked.

'You're mad, you barren bitch,' he stormed and pushed me down the stairs.

Bruised and shaken, I still had the voice to shout in reply so that all could hear, 'Barren I'm not by God, 'tis you who are impotent.' I was careless now of the consequences. Even the workhouse was better than being married to a murderer. But I had made a bad mistake, for blood is stronger than water and Will, who had heard it all, was outraged on his brother's behalf and determined to protect him from the scalding tongue of his wife.

I couldn't believe it. They were binding me and marching me to the Court House. The insults I flung at them in return brought neighbours to their doors to see what was causing the commotion. I swore at the neighbours too, for why would no one take my part? The magistrates also, smarting from my abuse, totally overlooked the injustice I had received from my husband in spite of my bruises. Nevertheless I expected they would be content with a reprimand but to my amazement they declared I was a 'scold' and sentenced me to the ducking stool.

'Not the ducking stool!' I cried, 'By God, 'tis not been used for years, let me be.' But the crowd was already excited, cheering at the prospect of my shame and they were already wheeling out the stool. Such a simple machine with its platform on four wheels of solid wood, yet what a humiliating instrument of torture! I gazed in horror at the long movable beam with its dreadful wooden seat at one end swinging ominously between the two posts embedded in the platform.

They were lowering the seat and pushing me into it. I clawed and bit them to no avail, for there was no escape. To my horror, I was being swung into the air.

'Wheel Jane Corran round the town so women can witness the punishment for a scold and curb their tongues!' shouted a hateful magistrate.

I felt sick as I was swivelled round in the chair, folk jumping to grab at my feet, some even hurling rotten eggs at me. One such caught me in the face and the vile stuff dripped down my nose and into my mouth making me vomit. Amidst the jeering, I heard the Quakers calling for me to repent. They meant well, but they are so narrow-minded; they have even called Master Williams 'a drunken fornicating curate', which couldn't be further from the truth. I wished I hadn't thought of him. Oh God, I prayed, don't let him be in the crowd to witness my shame, but if he were there, he was lost in the blur of upturned faces. I was only dimly aware of being trundled down New Street, past the gaol and then, Lud help me, past our house. Surely that was my poor old mother hobbling to the door to see me pass. No more telling me to be grateful. Oh God that I should bring such shame upon her! Wasn't the punishment of being ducked in the river enough without this humiliating parade? Pray God it was nearly over, for we were at New Street Turnpike Gate, which led north to Kenwater.

I had expected to feel relief at the sight of the river, but instead I was seized with terror. I tried to steel myself against the shock of the cold water. I feared I wouldn't be able to breathe when submerged. Shaking with fear, I glimpsed my husband's leering face as he led the shouting, 'Duck the scold! Duck her!'

The movement of the trolley beneath me stopped; I was suspended over the river. Then they swung me out. Was I really so far from the bank? Suddenly I was plunged into the icy depths, separated it seemed from my scream echoing above as though it belonged to someone else while the river thrust its watery fist into my throat. Then, heavy with water, I was being lifted again and ducked again. A large soggy shape was sticking to my face. In panic I snatched at it as the stool reared into the air. I blinked to clear the water from my eyes to see what I was clutching: it was John's hat—with the bullet hole in it. Even in my exhausted state, I managed to feel triumphant. Here was the evidence that would hang the bastard, even Will couldn't deny that. Through bleary eyes I searched the crowd for them as I was lowered to the ground, but couldn't see them.

Master Williams was now there, however, speaking urgently to the magistrates who, typically, were plainly ignoring him. 'Damn you bloody bastards, damn the lot of you!' I shouted lest they should think their cruel sport had affected me. They must not think they'd got the better of Jenny Pipes, or Jane Corran if I must be saddled with his name. I was ready to swear at them all with my dying breath.

But the entertainment was over, the crowd dispersed. Few wanted to face me once I was lowered and released. They were now ashamed, no doubt. The hateful ducking stool was wheeled away with the magistrates making self-righteous noises about my deserving my punishment because I was still swearing.

There was a hand on my arm and a blanket being put round my shoulders. 'That must never happen again, Jenny,' Master Williams was saying. 'I'll never let it happen, believe me. That ducking stool belongs in a museum.'

That may be, I thought bitterly, but that won't stop Jenny Pipes going down in history as the last person to suffer the indignity of the ducking stool, will it?

The Best of Wives

published in *The Hereford Journal*, 5 July 1809

A man had once a vicious wife
(A most uncommon thing in life)
His days and nights were spent in strife
Unceasing

Her tongue went glibly all day long
Sweet contradictions still her song
And all the poor man did was wrong
And ill done

A truce without doors or within
From speeches long as statesmen spin,
Or rest from her eternal din
He found not

He ev'ry soothing art display'd;
Try'd of what stuff her skin was made:
Failing in all, to heaven he pray'd
To take her.

Poem displayed in Leominster's Museum:

There stands my friend in yonder pool
An engine called the ducking stool
By legal power commanded down
The joy and terror of the town

If jarring females kindly strife
Give language foul or lug the coif
If noisy dames should once begin
To drive the house with horrid din
'Away you cry you'll grace the stool
We'll teach you how your tongue to rule,'
Down in the deep the stool descends
But here at first we miss our ends
She mounts again and rages more
Than ever vixen did before.
If so, my friend, then let her take
A second turn into the lake
And rather than your patience lose
Thrice and again repeat the dose
No brawling wives, no furious wenches
No fire so hot but water quenches.

The Dragon of Mordiford

 smell human meat. I am fed to fatness on deer from my forest and sheep from the fields of men. It is not hunger that I feel but a massive instinct to kill and devour mankind. My forked tongue darts out, dripping saliva from my slavering jaws. Fire belches from my stomach. The air turns sulphurous and explodes into swirling flame.

Down below in the village of Mordiford they will see smoke gushing from my cavern in Haugh Wood and they will quake in fear.

Desperate to sink my teeth into their succulent flesh, I heave my long cumbersome body out of my cave. My legs are bowed with the weight, my griffinlike wings must take the strain. I claw the trees as I rise above the clouds of my own foul breath, only to roar with frustration as I sink onto my familiar track to the river. They call it Serpent's Lane as though they know that I yearn to be a beast of the air, yet my wings lack the power and I am doomed to go forever on my belly. But I am no giant worm, for what worm ever left giant footprints in powdered ash?

It's all downhill now. Nothing grows on this path, I have seen to that. Either side scorched grass crackles as it meets my rasping breath.

Soon I will see their blackened farms and burned orchards. Already the smell of their fear mingles with that of their flesh. They are running from the fields where they labour in vain to their women, screaming in their timbered houses. But what use are wooden houses against my fiery fumes?

The thought of their women makes my dragonish bowels rise up, my bestial liver stir. I rear up and display my green and gold scaled belly as though to a she-dragon, for I cannot forget the girl-child they called Maud.

I was newly born when she found me—no bigger than a cucumber and bright green. She took me from the forest to her human lair. She stroked my bristly scales and reared me on the milk of cows. That's why I never swallow cows whole—I bite off their milk sacks and let the cool liquid trickle down my flaming throat.

Dragons grow fast—infinitely faster than puny men. They made her get rid of me. Freedom was what they called my eviction, the fools. That was years, or is it centuries ago? Still I roar her name but she never answers.

They suffer for it, the cruel ones who offered a beast a man's pleasure and then snatched it away. Rage consumes me. I lick the trees to console my flaming tongue and my eyes turn rheumy with my own smoke.

I must drink to cool the boiling inferno in my belly. Every evening it's the same. This raging thirst must be quenched before I feed.

I emerge from the foggy trees where one river obligingly meets another to supply my need. I am an elemental creature, a lizard of the earth, winged like birds of the air and full of fire. However, I see my reflection only in water. Water is my other self. In the raging torrent is a dragon's fury. It is my life-blood and I need to drink.

They know my habits. Here is a futile offering to appease my anger, but what use is a barrel of apple juice to a dragon? They

have left it unattended for they dare not look at me—they will be paralysed if they look into my lidless eyes.

My nostrils twitch. The smell is wrong—there is a man inside this barrel! The arrow flies out of the hole before I realise what is happening.

Excruciating pain. I roll and writhe. The earth quakes with my roaring. Death to the dragonslayer I roar and spew poison, for he must die first—caught in his own trap where he chokes to death from my fumes. His suffering is unheard whilst my death throes uproot trees and deafen the world.

Deep in my cavernous heart a furious fire is extinguished. My carcass crashes into the river where the waters rise and envelop me. I become one with the current and the flood.

In Mordiford they rejoice and paint my picture on their church wall, reporting my death in verse beneath it:

This is the true effigies of that strange
Prodigious monster, which out of the woods did range;
In Eastwood it was by Garson's hand slain,
A truth which old mythologists maintaine

I see it all as I slide beneath the old bridge. Centuries pass. I hear them ridicule my image. The memory of Man is short. They say I am unreal, that I never lived, but I grow to mammoth proportions and my identity seeps into the little river Pentaloe, born like my dragon self in the depths of Haugh Wood.

The raging of my waters turns the sky black. My voice is heard challenging the thunder, my scything tail cutting the air is mistaken for lightning. My watery skin bursts into a wave twenty feet high. I seethe through the valley, tossing tons of rock down from the hills—I will destroy Mordiford. I will flood, tear and swallow their homes, livestock and futile machinery.

Cloudburst after cloudburst inflame my turbulent waters. I savage a barn; it surrenders. In hideous triumph my current seizes the huge fragments and hurls them at the miller's cottage. I pulverize his drowned body, choking on the woman and children who tangle with weed in my spluttering jaws.

There is the church parading my image. Its tower must fall. I spit, spume and spew great masses of rock and timbers over its stubborn foundations, yet still it defies my raging torrent.

In frustration I submerge the fields, uproot the trees and turn the old bridge into an island in a vast sea. Even when the waters go down, the scars will remain. And the dragon is always near ... eternally hungry. A monster's fury has condemned Mordiford to floods until the end of the world when dragons must die.

They cannot escape. They have only to look up to the Woolhope hills to see me, crouching on the horizon. There is my long green body, my spiky scales bristling and my breath misting the creases in my hoary skin ...

Adam de Orleton

y baptism set the pattern for my life. My parents were honoured by Lord Edmund Mortimer, their landlord for Orleton Manor, agreeing to be my godfather and attending my baptism in person.

Years afterwards I would gaze into the holy water in the font and see my life mirrored there. Lord Mortimer must have stood here while I screamed the devil out of my soul as the priest made the watered cross on my forehead. The nine tall figures carved round the bowl would have witnessed it all. I would run my chubby finger up the cold stone, wondering who they were. Was that St. Peter holding a key?

I remember him asking me questions about the font when he came to Orleton church to celebrate the crushing of the Welsh rebellion, in which my father had been killed. Lord Edmund little knew that he himself was to be slain by the Welsh near Builth. At the time I was naive enough to think that he was just interested in the font but later I realised he was testing me. My mother had told him his fatherless godson was a 'promising' boy and he was thinking of my future.

'Who are these, Adam?' he had asked, indicating the nine stone figures.

'Monks, sir,' I answered, 'for they're holding bibles and candles in their long thin fingers and they're standing between pillars such as you see in a monastery.'

'Are you sure? I think they're holding swords.'

Swords and bibles? I thought it unlikely but I answered deferentially. 'It may be so, my lord.'

'Are all your monks the same, Master Adam?'

'No, my lord. That one has straight hair parted in the middle, the rest have curls. I like him best.'

'Why?'

'Because he's not afraid to be different.'

I was startled by his laughter. I didn't think I'd said anything amusing. 'Do you mind that, young Adam!' He roared. 'See you follow his example!'

It was Edmund's son, Roger Mortimer, who told me later that same day that his father was sending me to the monastic school in Hereford. Admiration shone in Roger's eyes and I responded to it. I was the big boy about to embark on a great adventure.

It had been a long hot summer and there was a hint of autumn in the air when the time came for departure. My mother took my belongings and valuables from the oak chest that had been my father's and handed them to the maid-servant, who in turn put them in saddle-bags for the pack horses to carry—all the way to Hereford.

I was ready early. There was time to walk up the lane to the church and say farewell to the village. Memories flooded back. I remembered taking Roger to a small cave in the hill above Orleton. At first it was a bore looking after Lord Mortimer's son during those special visits his father made to my parents. 'A giant lived here once,' I told Roger when I had persuaded him into the cave, 'and here are his bones!' There were some enormous bones but I didn't really believe in the giant. Roger did though, he was much younger of course and it was unfair of me to frighten him, but I was

beginning to enjoy his company. I felt more confident when he was around.

I smiled at the memory of the giant's cave as I walked past the peasants' thatched cottages with their roughly finished walls. Most were in good repair but the one near the church was neglected because the old man had been sick for some time. The other peasants were already fetching scythes, rakes and sickles from their sheds before setting off to mow the barley or cut the wheat. I greeted them all courteously as Lord Mortimer would have wished.

'God bless 'ee, Master Adam!' called the old man from the end cottage, as he leant on his stick while his bedraggled hens pecked hungrily at his feet. His face was a mass of running sores in spite of the dwarf mallow gruel my mother prepared especially for him, to heal his ulcerous skin. He would not see another winter. 'When you return, young master, I be buried with me feet next to the churchyard gate. I be first away at the Resurrection! Don't 'ee forget that!'

I tried to laugh but my heart was heavy as I stood in the churchyard beside my father's grave, looking across at the familiar skyline of Clee Hill.

'Is it all Clee Hill, Father?' I remembered asking him.

'Indeed it is lad,' he had replied. 'It goes down into a little scoop, then up again but 'tis all the same hill.'

It looked formidable in the early morning, no longer friendly but like a lion at rest with an arched back. I sought solace in the church, grappling with the stiff iron door handle. Finally it swung open. A few paces inside and I was standing beneath the belltower to find a bird at my feet, newly dead, its blue-tinted feathers still shiny. I shivered. Were there no good omens for me?

In the distance I heard horses being led from the stables, their hooves striking the cobbles of the courtyard, and the grooms' chatter as they loaded the packhorses. It was time to go. Hereford lay twenty miles south of Orleton—a daunting distance. ''Tis not far Adam; 'tis not the end of the world,' Roger had said. Though the younger, he had travelled more widely and I had grown to trust him implicitly. ''Tis not far ,' I repeated to myself.

My cheek was wet with my mother's tears as I focused fiercely on the horses' steamy breath. I had to hold my own emotions in check. I must not let the Mortimers down in front of Canon John.

It was a relief to get started, to feel my horse between my thighs. The road was lost in the mist and the marshy ground, hard with early frost, near the hamlet of Ashton. It was a lonely journey along the track and especially eerie in the Long Wood, where I rode close to Canon John. We laughed bravely at deer surprised at our invasion of their territory, as we trampled over seeding grass and nettles, following the track through wooded countryside with barely a cottage in sight. Eventually woods gave way to open land tarnished with cut hay which peasants were binding before carrying it to their lord's barn. Two men were walking across the field, each bearing two enormous sheaves to put on the great pile. Early sunlight was already playing tricks on the grassland, splashing bright green patches on shaded black.

Our horses quickened their pace as though recognising the Roman road running straight and true across the Lugg Valley. After wading through the Humber Brook, we drew nearer to the river itself close to the remains of Sutton Walls, finally crossing it at Wergin's Ford. Nearby was Wergin's Stone. 'Say a prayer as you pass yon stone, Master Adam,' shouted Canon John, 'they say the devil moves it: you'll see it in one place one day, and somewhere else the next.' My horse suddenly shied and I was seized with fear, the stone was taller than I and infinitely heavier. 'God deliver me from the Old 'Un!' I cried. Then into my mind came the shining eyes of Roger Mortimer. To this day, I swear I could feel his hand on my arm. I was no longer afraid.

Not long afterwards, we climbed the last rise and I was looking down on Hereford with its mighty cathedral tower and surrounded by its new city wall. 'We'll not be crossing the ditch, Master Adam,' Canon John informed me, 'for St. Guthlac's is outside the walls.'

Resentment turned to apprehension as we passed beneath the priory's stone gateway into an orchard whose trees heavy with apples consoled me with thoughts of home. That lasted until I entered the stately chambers and large melancholy chapel. My sense of awe was then rapidly to turn to grasping ambition, for Orleton was truly behind me. My new life had begun and I meant to use the opportunity which the patronage of the Mortimers afforded me.

111

Thus I passed from the monastic school at Hereford to Oxford, and later to Paris and Orléans. My patron's generosity ensured a smooth ride. I had no need to protest in Paris streets with bands of needy students crying 'Pain pour Dieu aux escoliers!' By 1307, I had become one of the king's clerks, well versed in civil and canon law.

Meanwhile Roger had become eighth Lord of Wigmore on the death of his father, but, as he was under age, the king had made him the ward of Piers Gaveston, the chief friend of the Prince of Wales. That was an error of judgement on the part of good old King Edward. Gaveston was a brainless upstart as the king eventually realised and banished him from court.

Fortunately Edward did recognize a shrewd ecclesiastic when he saw one and used my administrative skills. If only his son had inherited such wisdom, but alas, King Edward II was no friend of mine. He only had time for empty-headed flatterers like Gaveston. Once the old king was dead, the young Edward was able to bring his favourite back to the Court—and into his bed. The king would then delight in lavishing wet kisses on his beloved 'Perrot's' lips before the assembled company of which I was one. Gaveston's subsequent marriage to the king's niece, and the king's own marriage to Isabella of France, raised a few eyebrows till the king quickly dispelled any doubts by announcing that he preferred the couch of Perrot to his bridal bed. Needless to say, he continued to caress Gaveston in front of the Queen.

I was troubled not so much by the king's behaviour but my own reaction to it. My hand would inadvertently stray to my chin as I watched him stroke Gaveston's beard and I felt angry—oh, so angry—but not on the queen's behalf, least not until I realised how Roger felt about Isabella. His brow would grow dark at the mention of Gaveston.

For the next ten years I was rarely in England. The king, perhaps sensing my disapproval, used me to represent him at the Papal Curia. I only travelled back to England once or twice a year and learnt, in due course, that Gaveston had been murdered and the queen had borne Edward a son. The new favourites were the Despensers, father and son. They were Marcher lords with greed and ambition equal to Gaveston's but they were also clever. What a threat they constituted to the other Lords Marcher—especially to the Mortimers who were by now the king's bitter enemies.

While discord fermented, the pope, sensing my disquiet, nominated me as Bishop of Hereford. I was delighted for this meant that I was going home to Mortimer country, to a city largely controlled by members of my family, who took it in turn to hold the office of Chief Steward.

The king was furious. He had wanted to appoint Thomas of Cherleton but the pope had overruled him to Roger's delight. 'It speaks well for thee, Adam,' he exclaimed as he embraced me, 'that thy preferment comes from the pope, not from our apology for a king!'

'Indeed Roger, I am glad to be with thee,' I answered, 'I have but two loyalties on this earth and I shall always be true to both—to Pope John XXII and to thee, my dear lord.'

Never was a man's loyalty to be more tested. My return to Hereford meant that my fate was to be inextricably linked to Roger's and to his fight with the Despensers, Edward's new favourites. Events were moving fast for Hugh Despenser had claimed Gower, ignoring the 'custom of the March', and insisted that English customs applied to the Marcher lands. The Mortimers had to act to protect their power. Thus in 1321, four years after my appointment as bishop, I found myself with Roger and his uncle, Roger of Chirke, at St. Albans demanding the expulsion of the hated Despensers from the Court. It was useless of course.

Later Roger summoned me to a secret conference at Bosbury. ''Tis war, Adam,' he declared, 'I need thy support and reinforcements. Mortimer must uphold the custom of the March. The king hath no right to disregard it. I know thou will'st be with me, for thou can'st never be against me.' Nor could I. I promised to despatch men-at-arms to him at once.

'Thou art a good friend, Adam,' he acknowledged and then uncharacteristically averted his eyes from mine. 'I have another favour to ask of thee.'

The air was charged with emotion. Was he wiping a tear from his eye? 'Only ask!' I insisted.

'Look to the queen, she may need thee.' I controlled my disappointment but agreed readily. I became a catalyst for royal contempt with the king publicly accusing me of advising the queen to 'withdraw herself from him'. Of course, it had nothing to do with her infatuation for Roger Mortimer! It was I, Adam of Orleton, who was disgracing the sacred ministry by driving the queen's party to the utmost lengths of rebellion by simply using the words 'my head acheth' in my sermon at Oxford. If folk interpreted this phrase as meaning that the head of the kingdom was in disorder and it was up to individual members to provide for their own welfare independently, then so be it! Anyway, the king's position was rapidly weakening without my help and he was forced to agree to the exile of his dastardly favourites, temporarily at least.

My commitment to the Mortimer's cause had finally branded me a traitor in the eyes of the king. I was summoned before the magnates of his kingdom in Parliament and tried for high treason. The king personally brought the charge. I can still hear his bitter and vindictive whine. I bore his scurrilous accusation in silence, but the hatred within my soul for that wimp of a king was great indeed. The ignorant fool had broken the law—a bishop can't be tried by a civil tribunal, and I told him so. 'With respect, my lord the king,' I said, 'I cannot answer this grave charge unless authorised by the archbishop of Canterbury, whose suffragan I am and who alone, after the pope, is my judge.'

The archbishop then entered the hall with ten bishops all holding their crosses in front of them, and took me away—for were not the privileges of all his clergy at stake? The king could not proceed. I was free.

Unfortunately Roger fared worse. He had been forced to surrender when the king rallied his forces and defeated the Lords Marcher in Wales. Roger and his uncle were in prison in the Tower for two years. I had one purpose, and one alone—with God's help to rescue Roger, but I had to bide my time until Roger's uncle was too infirm to attempt the perils of an escape. Without him, Roger's chances would be considerably greater.

In absolute secrecy, I made the arrangements with my customary diligence and thoroughness. It was to take place on the night of 1 August, the Festival of St. Peter ad Vincula. 'Grant freedom, O Lord, to thy servant Roger Mortimer,' I prayed, 'as Thou did'st to thy Apostle, Peter.'

My prayer was answered. The guards emptied their possets which my spy had drugged. Beneath the walls of the Tower a boat was ready to carry Roger across the Thames where waited two grooms with horses to take him to the sea where a boat would carry him to France.

Risking Roger's displeasure, I disobeyed his implicit instructions. He did not realise until we reached the coast that one of those grooms in the darkness was myself. There I threw off my cloak and held in my arms the man for whom I had risked so much.

Ironically his words on recognising me didn't concern my safety, nor his own, but that of the queen. 'Is Isabella safe?' was all he said.

She was safe indeed—in France where he would shortly join her. I knew how the king had ill-used her and that she too hated the Despensers. Hadn't I myself suggested that she invade England and take the crown for her son, fourteen year old Prince Edward? What I didn't realise then—how can I have been so naive?—was the intensity of her desire for Roger. Truly she drove him into her bed. His months in the Tower had only served to whet her passion. As a bishop, I was entitled to frown on their adultery, yet I did not—for who was I to cast a stone?

Inevitably Isabella's Court in Paris became a focus for exiles plotting to rid our realm of the Despensers. She was a bold one. Grudgingly I admired her for defying her brother, the King of France, when she openly took Roger as her lover. As for the invasion of England, it was more like a triumphal march following her landing in Suffolk with her young son. England was sick of Edward and his sycophants and welcomed Isabella with open arms.

I became her chief adviser. Roger wished it. I spoke in Parliament in January 1327 of the follies and imbecilities of the king. 'If the queen returns to him,' I told the people, 'he will murder her!' Carried away by my own eloquence and elated by Roger's gratitude, I failed to recognize my own inadequacy, only the king's.

The queen and Prince Edward were my guests at the Bishop's Palace in Hereford—their troops were stationed at the castle. While we were dining in my Great Hall, news came that the king and the younger Despenser had been captured.

The next step was to secure the king's consent for his son's immediate succession in his stead. I put this to him at Kenilworth, where he was being held prisoner. If he didn't abdicate in favour of his son, I told him, he would be dethroned to make room for a stranger. I experienced, I regret, a sadistic pleasure in watching the semi-conscious wretch, supported in the arms of Henry of Lancaster and the Bishop of Winchester, receive my ultimatum.

I had done my part and now I wanted no more of it for I could not bear Roger's happiness in Isabella. My mind was troubled and I set off for Avignon to my Holy Father, the pope. There I begged His Holiness to forgive me for what I had done, for what I feared I might do—and most of all for the misgivings of my heart.

The pope sensed my distress. 'God is merciful my son. To ease your torment, I grant your confessor the right to give you, being penitent, plenary forgiveness of your sins at the hour of your death.'

Did he know, I wonder, that while Edward lived, Isabella and Roger would never be secure? I must bear the cross of Edward's murder for their sake—for Roger's sake.

I approached it as though I were writing a sermon: planning and structure controlling emotion. During a visit to Berkeley Castle, where the king was imprisoned, I casually remarked to his keepers, Lord Maltravers and Thomas Gourney, that it were better for the king to die 'naturally' than to suffer the consequences of his folly.

'If he died thus, my lord, there would be no marks on his body?' queried Thomas.

'Even so, good fellow,' I replied.

Shortly afterwards I despatched a letter to the incorrigible pair. 'Edwardum occidere nolite timere bonum est.' I wrote, and deliberately inserted the suggestion of a comma before and after 'timere'. My message could thus have two meanings, dependent on the position of the comma. 'Fear not to kill the king, 'tis good he die', or 'Kill not the king, 'tis good to fear the worst.'

That night I slept fitfully, desperately trying to wake from a recurring nightmare. I was thrusting a red hot spit into Edward's bowels. 'And that's for Mortimer!' I kept yelling as his flesh heaved in agony and unearthly cries of pain rent the air. I awoke sobbing in a wet bed, crying for comfort, for Roger. Grim reality denied me both.

The two murderers fled, of course, beyond the sea to escape the consequence of their 'stupid reading.' I declared angrily that 'anyone could have seen that the comma should have been after 'nolite''.

I was appointed one of the Council of Regency for the young king. But life was intolerable and I couldn't look Roger in the face. We never discussed Edward's murder, not least the nature of it for it was too dangerous. The satisfaction, nay even the horror of his reaction was denied me.

Back to my Holy father I went. 'Release me from Hereford, Your Holiness,' I pleaded. He understood. I would return as Bishop of Worcester.

Before I left Mortimer country, I had a pilgrimage to make—to Orleton. And so I stood beside the font where I was baptized, where I had been questioned by Edmund Mortimer before he sent me to the monastic school. So much had happened, yet the implacable gaze of the nine stone figures was unchanged. I bent down and peered into the hard face of the one with the straight hair, parted in the middle.

'I'm not afraid to be different, either,' I said—the stone seemed to soften into the features of Edmund Mortimer and then melt, inevitably, into those of Roger.

It was time to be honest and to face the truth: Roger Mortimer was a part of Adam Orleton. It was a union neither man nor woman could break.

John Kyrle of Ross

ow many of us fulfil the expectations of our parents? From the moment I was born on 22 May 1637 they intended me for the Bar—to follow in my father's footsteps. My family had a distinguished record, for we were descended from John Hampden, whilst my father was a notable barrister, as well as representing Leominster in the Parliament of 1640.

As for me, I followed this route as far as leaving grammar school for Balliol College, Oxford. But once there study and reading suddenly seemed irrelevant in the England of 1654. In the fertile climate of Oxford there was so much to discuss, far into the night. Would Cromwell reform the slow and cumbersome law courts which so often seemed to favour the rich? Would he dare to become King Oliver? Would he ever find an acceptable way to govern England? Dissatisfaction with his army was aired at many an intellectual feast, but politics was a dangerous game and I learnt to listen and reserve judgment. Nevertheless, debate distracted me and I never took my degree.

To compensate, I presented the university with a silver tankard, a loving cup that held five pints and was inscribed: Poculum Charitatis ex dono Johannis

Kyrle de Ross in agro Herefordiensi et hujus Collegii Socii Commensalis, (A Loving Cup from the gift of John Kyrle in the land of Hereford and a dining fellow of this college.) I could ill afford it but I economised strictly to meet the cost. I was already tall and thin when I went up to Oxford, but like a bean pole when I came down. My graduation might not be recorded, but my association with the college would be.

I never practised law, not even when I returned to Ross to the estates I had inherited from my father. I am not an overly rich man; my yearly income is some £600 a year and that includes the proceeds from timber felled in Dymock Wood, hardly a fortune in my century.

Still, I have a rare talent compared to other country squires: I know how to use money. I never run into debt, pay my taxes promptly and do much, I let it be known, with little cash.

With people I am less successful. I unwittingly keep them at a distance for something makes me reluctant to expose, or even understand my true feelings. I draw a veil of dignity over them which none can penetrate. Success, even happiness I decided, lay in using my financial skill. In this way I can help people and win their respect, if not their friendship.

Neighbours wonder at my austere lifestyle. 'Do you know,' they gossip, 'the Squire of Ross only has one dish for his Sunday dinner?' No-one of similar social standing sits down to a single dish. My Sunday dinner of a rump of beef with vegetables from my own garden, is excessively frugal. 'Od's bud, enough is as good as a feast!' I say.

I send bread from my own table to anyone in need. To ensure the poor receive their daily bread, I collect the corn tolls from the market on their behalf. I have it baked into bread and delivered daily to the almshouses by the church.

My popularity extends to my own class too. On market and fair days neighbouring gentlemen and farmers always come to dine. My

home is conveniently placed at the centre of the town, opposite the new market hall, whilst outside my back door runs the cobbled coaching road.

As I sit at my upstairs window I look straight out on the new hall with its splendid red sandstone pillars, and which I saw being built. Outside the hall traders and pedlars hustle for position. Through the crowd I see my friends emerge, ready to share my beer and cider—the best drink of all! They'll not expect wine at my table.

How I love those long evenings when my invited guests come to dine. There are frequently thirteen round my table—I'm not super-stitious. Give me my oak armchair, one of my two pipes full of tobacco and company who will tell me a good story. I laugh loudly—too loudly; they see a confident fellow. But when they leave I find it hard to disguise my distress, for I am alone again.

Many visitors come for professional advice. They appeal to the Man of Ross as they call me, to settle their quarrels. I provide a simpler and more direct justice than the courts and, in 1683, I was elected Sheriff of Herefordshire. I am the Law in Ross, but at the same time I am a man of the people.

Folk respect me all the more because I have no great fortune or connections. I'm always seen in the same outfit: my brown suit and a short bushy wig. Everyone knows I work on the land with my own labourers—I am the friend of all men, but close to no man.

They trust me with their money, and why not? Giving to charity and contributing to my schemes to improve our town are worthy activities.

'Od's bud, it's time we had an efficient water supply,' I say. Some didn't believe my plan would work but it has. Water from the River Wye is driven up by an engine through the dry rocky ground on which Ross stands high above the river and provides a fountain in the Prospect. Here there is a fine view of the Wye's horseshoe bend, with the old stone bridge, Wilton village and castle completing the picture. 'The Prospect is just the place for a public park,' I say. 'Od's bud, everyone should have the opportunity to enjoy the view and peace here!' A few ornamental shrubs and trees will turn it into a delightful garden.

The Wye, though, is not always tranquil. I was down there once during the floods, when they brought this boy's body ashore. The

120

distraught father was warning his other sons to keep away from the river, when someone remarked, 'Let'm alone, no-one else'll be drowned this year—the river's had its due.' Immediately I leant the father my support lest superstitious ignorance lead to another tragedy, and there and then I vowed to rebuild the causeway linking Ross to Wilton Bridge. That way I can ensure that the road remains above flood level. It will also give me a chance to plant more trees.

I love trees, especially elms. Those I've planted in the church-yard will be there hundreds of years after my death. Trees are faithful to the end, and beyond.

I'm given to dozing in the carved stone summer house in my garden when the weather's warm and the wind plays in the trees, soothing me into sleep.

The trees turn to tall shadows along a road. I am riding hard, my black cloak billows behind me, my long black curly wig ripples against my neck, the mask tightens on my face. The rhythm of my horse's flanks increases between my thighs. Gone are the aging cramps—I am free; I am ecstatic. My flesh seethes with excitement. Is that the stagecoach? Lord John will have their purses soon.

I wake in a cold sweat roaring, 'Stand and Deliver!' Has anyone heard? No, the servants keep away from the summer house for they know it is my quiet place.

I must stop dreaming, though how real it seemed, and visit the old dame at the school for she'll be expecting my weekly visit. When I arrive I congratulate her on her three pupils who have learnt to read. Enthusiastically they dip their quills to show me they have moved on to writing now. 'No ink blots—or you'll be punished!' she says. Tom Spenser is growing fast, but he still can't recite the Lord's Prayer by heart. 'Od's bud, Od's bud,' I roar, 'I'll mend you.'

His tear-stained face looks into mine. I pat his hair compassion-ately; the squashed lice stick to my hand. There is a concoction in my cupboard at home that will cure that. 'Tell me the Lord's prayer next week, Tom' I say, 'and I'll ensure you'll become apprenticed.' People can be planted like trees, but pruning is essential.

Before I visit the Spensers' cottage, I must go to the church as I am carrying some money for the fund for the spire, the appeal for which was my idea. Heavy coins from many purses jangle in my pocket as I walk up to St. Mary's, acknowledging the greetings of the townsfolk I pass. Such popularity has its price, for envy of my position breeds enemies. For example, my relatives, the Gibsons of Abbeydore, never have a kind word for me and tell folk that I'm vain and ostentatious.

Even as I reflect on their hostility I feel a hand on my shoulder. Gruff words follow. 'You're wanted in Gloucester, Master Kyrle, to answer the magistrate's questions about the stage robbed last night on the king's highway. Just step into that coach yonder, and we'll be on our way.'

I know the magistrate in Gloucester for I have dined with the man! How embarrassing! A plague on that rascal Gibson, this must be his doing. The sixteen miles to Gloucester seem endless, but news of my problem has reached the ears of friends in Ross, three of whom arrive at the magistrate's shortly after I do and before the cash taken from my pocket can even be counted.

'Master Kyrle always keeps his capital in cash,' they exclaim. 'You must have heard of his lavish gifts to charity. He has done more for Ross than anyone living or dead.'

My release is speedily secured, but the experience is salutary. Back in Ross I spend time in prayer at the church, having safely delivered the appeal money. Then I find myself visiting the town prison where I find the stench is appalling. Grumbling ragbags and tattered felons grab at my clothes. I can more readily identify with the debtors, educated men, some of them. You need education to fall into debt and good common sense to avoid it.

'I have a plan,' I tell them, 'to free you from prison and re-establish you in life.'

The least I can do. For who am I but a humble man. Please don't commemorate me in sanctimonious verse, but see me as I am, a lonely sinner who wishes to atone.

Peter de Aquablanca of Stretton Sugwas

believe in God. Well of course I do, for I'm a bishop. I believe in Jesus Christ. Interpreting His parables is food for my intellect. Witness the parable of the talents exemplified in my own career— astute financiers like me are rare indeed! But I also believe in Peter de Aquablanca.

I was born of embarrassingly servile parents in Savoy, in Aigue-blanche in the Tarentaise, to be precise. I wasn't going to settle for a peasant's life and my labour was soon rewarded: I became confidential clerk to William of Savoy. William was ambitious too and was planning to marry his niece, Eleanor of Provençe, to the English king, Henry III.

We sailed over to England in 1236—not that I could speak a word of English, for who would demean himself to learn the language of the peasant and the wet nurse when they spoke French at the English court. Even the King of England despised the English and filled his court with Frenchmen. His Chancellor, Peter des Roches, was an example to us all, for old Peter brought over all his relatives and friends from France and they are now rich landowners in England.

Through the king's love of foreigners, and his eventual marriage to Eleanor, my future was soon assured.

I was William's 'clericus familiaris', his confidential secretary. I was confidential alright. I had been in young Eleanor's bed! One must do what one must do. I took stock of the large mole on her left buttock—a word at the English Court could have finished the alliance with Provence there and then.

Of course I'd never reveal my intimate knowledge of Queen Eleanor. It was stimulating, however, to note her discomfort in my presence and she wanted me out of the Court. 'Can'st thou not give Peter a bishopric, my lord?' she begged. The bishopric of Durham took my fancy—a good jumping-off ground for higher office, they say! I got my bishopric, but it wasn't Durham. It was a place I'd barely heard of—on the borders of Wales. I was to be bishop of Hereford.

I didn't concern myself with the place for I was too busy organizing my splendid consecration in St. Paul's Cathedral which was to take place on 23 December, 1240. No expense was to be spared for there is nothing more edifying than ceremony in an ornate church; it is food for the soul. That is why I encouraged the king to rebuild Westminster Abbey. ''Tis time,' I told him, 'for a lighter and more gracious style of building with pointed arches.'

With my mind brimming with architectural refinements, I was obliged to leave for my diocese. It was a journey from the sublime to the ridiculous—from the French-speaking English Court to barbaric, wild Hereford.

I had to import a friendly crowd into the city or live amongst semi-savages. I opted for the former and made my precocious nephew John, dean of the cathedral. I promised all my other friends and relatives parishes and stalls in the cathedral if they came with me to the city. They came. Blood is thicker than water and I needed their support if I was to remain sane amongst uncouth foreign peasants.

Misunderstanding was inevitable, my interpreter already having difficulty with the broad Hereford speech and no understanding at

all of the barbaric tongue spoken in Wales. Even so, examples would have to be made and I wondered if the prison in the bishop's palace would be big enough to serve my needs.

The palace itself was next to the cathedral and totally unfortified. I was therefore unprotected—not a situation in which I would expect a king's counsellor and pope's bishop to find himself. I soon realised that I needed a bolt hole. As bishop I possessed many episcopal manors, of which my favourite was Stretton Sugwas, my summer palace I called it, three miles out of the city. Stretton Sugwas was not so much a hamlet as an occasional cottage or two along the track. It was a long straight track, for this was the Roman street, or Stretton, which joined the rough highway to Wales.

The land around the palace is relatively flat for the River Wye flows only a mile from my manor. The lake at Sugwas Pool has also taken advantage of the river valley. However, the green woods of Credenhill rise out of the fields behind my manor.

My first sight of the manor was memorable. My carriage suddenly lurched and swung right on to another track infinitely worse than the so-called Roman road. It bumped and splashed through the pot-holes until it became embedded in a deep rut. My interpreter then translated the words of the overwrought driver to the effect that my palace was in yonder copse. Evidently he wanted to make it clear that he had brought me within walking distance of the house.

'I have more confidence in my feet than in your horses,' I grumbled as my steward helped me down into the mud. We left the driver shouting foreign obscenities at his horses, urging them to pull harder, while a number of serfs, who seemed to have grown out of the trees, pushed the carriage from behind.

Where was the manor house? The trees hid it completely from view. I had a strange feeling that my enemies would never find me here. It was the only place in the diocese where I would feel safe. Even my canons wouldn't pursue me here to sort out their complaining parishes.

Next to the manor, but divided from it by its own band of trees, was the little Norman church. Behind the house a path followed a stream almost concealed by thick undergrowth before sprouting a bed of tall rushes. The stream widened as it hurried over protruding rocks. I could hear the water-wheel turning at the mill and the miller came out to greet me, for I was his lord and this was my mill.

Seeing the miller was like looking into a mirror. I was visibly shaken. He was grossly overweight and had an enormous wart on his nose. I couldn't take my eyes off it. I have similar growths inside my nose which protrude from my nostrils. But beware, those who have alluded to my nasal affliction have paid the price.

My similarity to the miller didn't end with his appearance. There was the way people regarded us. The villagers resented paying a fee for having corn ground in my mill. They knew he swapped the grain for that of a poorer quality and gave them short measure—but they could never catch him out as he was too cunning. Not as cunning as I though, for neither king nor pope could catch me out. It was a relief to find that here at Stretton Sugwas was a man more hated than myself.

As the estate reeve took me with my own steward and interpreter to the Big Meadow, I surprised myself by greeting the peasants with a wave of my hand as they scattered wheat seed in the open field. Was it the church bells ringing to welcome me that prompted this uncharacteristic gesture? The prior of Llanthony Secunda was the patron of the little church and he appointed its priest. In his eagerness to meet my wishes, (for my fearsome reputation had preceded me), he had selected a priest learned in both French and Latin tongues.

His carefully prepared sermons were tedious, however, and sent me to sleep. In truth, the summer heat made me sweat profusely, my gout was painful and the church was the only place where I felt relatively cool.

The Norman tympanum over the doorway was strangely comforting. It showed Samson astride a lion's back and vigorously pulling its jaws asunder with his hands. My body may be weak and clumsy, but Samson-like I can defy the Beast inherent in mankind—especially true of this uncivilised part of the world—for my mind is sharper and more lethal than that of any savage creature.

I was naturally often absent from Hereford in order to maintain my influence at court, where I helped increase the king's finances. Finding people who were eager to ingratiate themselves with the pope and the king, I'd persuade them to put their seals on my impressive blank charters. By filling in a few necessary details I soon created an agreement by which they were forced to 'lend' money to the king.

The king, in turn, was grateful. He called me his 'special councillor.' I became his treasurer and chief consultant on all state matters. Enormous sums of money were dispatched to Rome from our devout English king to his overlord, the pope, who even sent a cardinal to England to congratulate me on my loan scheme.

Of course, I paid my many friends and countrymen handsomely to carry on the business of the diocese in my absence. One such friend paid dearly for the privilege. Bernard was prior of a monastery in Champagne. He had recently agreed to look after my affairs in Hereford and received a knife in his back for his trouble. 'Saying Mass and murdered in my palace chapel?' I gasped when they told me. Unbelievable, but all too true. Worse, I dared not punish the perpetrators of the crime for fear of reprisals.

You can see why I was uneasy in my cathedral church—fearful of a knife in my own back. Desperately I made magnanimous gestures which the villeins would surely understand even if they couldn't speak my language. Out of my own pocket I gave generously to the poor and to the cathedral itself. Money, lands, ornaments and books—there was no limit to my generosity. God knows, I have tried to meet those barbarians halfway! After I'd fined the citizens of Hereford for encroaching on my rights, I returned them half the amount. I couldn't have been fairer than that, could I?

You'd have thought they'd have been grateful for the magnificent north transept I was building. I took my competent master stone mason (he was Norman, of course) to the new Westminster Abbey. 'I want twin straight-sided arches like those, reproduced in my north transept in Hereford,' I told him, 'and make sure each arch has three smaller arches surmounted with encircled quatrefoils.'

I suppose, in retrospect, I should never have expected gratitude from Hereford folk, for they can be suspicious of anything new— new meaning anything up to twenty years old!

Thick-skinned I may be, but enduring their hostility for twenty years was not my intention.

I should have liked to have lived permanently at Stretton Sugwas but it was on the Welsh side of the city. The Welsh might attack at

any time—provided they could find the house amongst the trees. But I had to spend some time in Hereford, for king and pope expected it. I did manage, however, to have frequent urgent business in France, to keep me away from my diocese as much as possible.

In 1262, I returned to Hereford to be greeted by old Ralph, the clerk of my chapel. He was an elderly Norman whose annual wage was a mere five shillings a year. (A pity he died before I could raise it).

'My lord,' he cried breathlessly, 'your household has fled, the Welsh rebels are said to have reached Eardisley.'

Baron Clifford had a castle at Eardisley and the prospect of that troublemaker at the mercy of the Welsh momentarily pleased me, but the horror of my own situation soon dawned. I needed confirmation of this news.

'Where is the dean? And my canons?'

'All fled, my lord.'

There was nothing for it but to follow their example.

'This is what comes of relying on Hereford and its pathetic city walls,' I muttered to Ralph as my carriage rolled towards Gloucester.

Unfortunately the king took a different view. Just my luck that he arrived in Hereford to organize his forces against the Welsh and found no bishop, no dean and no clergy!

'Bishops do not desert their dioceses! Return to Hereford forthwith with your clerics—or lose it!'

The king had spoken. It was no good making allowances for his poor health. He meant what he said and back we all went—for better or worse.

I reckoned there could be nothing worse than confronting Welsh invaders, but I was wrong. Within days of my reoccupying the palace, my butler came rushing indecorously into my private bedchamber.

'Sir Roger de Clifford is here m..my lord,' he spluttered. Scarcely had he spoken when that impudent baron burst into my bedchamber and commanded his men to take me in my bed! O, the humiliation! Holding my robe frantically about me, I was bundled into a cart with my silver and other treasures, and borne away to the dastardly baron's castle. Only later did I realise he was flaunting on his finger the ruby I had worn at my consecration.

It was small comfort to see my canons tied back to back in the cart in front as we hurried along the muddy road to Eardisley. We passed the turning into the Roman road that would have taken me to Stretton Sugwas in happier days. I strained my eyes to see my palace but it had wisely taken refuge amongst the trees.

I was imprisoned in Eardisley Castle for three months before the king took action on my behalf. Sir Roger had to pay a fine of 300 marks and do penance. Penance? The man was never penitent. May his soul rot in Hell!

'Forgive him!' ordered the king. My lips uttered the requisite words while my heart cursed him. After all, I was a sick man. Staying in that damp dungeon had played havoc with my health.

I went home to my native Savoy to recuperate. It was some years since I had been there. To my surprise, I realised that my collegiate church at Aiguebelle could actually learn something from Hereford Cathedral. Before I left I directed that the services there be conducted on the same lines as those in Hereford.

Once back in Hereford, the old fears returned. There was only one place to go—Stretton Sugwas, which, I argued, was healthier than the city.

So, in the quiet confines of my country palace, towards the end of November 1268, I dictated my will. My nephew, the dean of Hereford, had agreed to act as my chief executor. 'Thou can'st have my plain bible and two horses for thy trouble, John.' I said.

Skeletal trees closed round my house as daylight ebbed away on that November evening. Would the stars emerge as my clerk wrote my instructions in the flickering candlelight?

'The bulk of my wealth goes to the College of Canons I founded at home, in Aiguebelle, Savoy.' I insisted. 'Hereford can have my mitre. They didn't honour me in my lifetime, but I'll make sure they do after my death! My tomb must be exquisite. My effigy shall rest beneath a lofty canopy. It shall be delicately wrought. Italian craftsmen must be summoned to fashion it—I do not want any of these uncouth local folk tampering with it................

Simon de Freine of Sutton St. Nicholas and Sutton St. Michael

aster Simon de Freine, the prior will see you shortly,' said the young monk.

I was a little put out. I had arrived on time for my appointment at St. Guthlac's Monastery and had resisted the temptation to dally in its spacious gardens and orchards. I hadn't even paused to wash my feet in the Eigne, the rivulet that ran beneath the walls of this monastic Garden of Eden—and I had walked seven miles from my home in Sutton to see the prior. Prior? He was more like a prince judging by his domain. It was hard to equate this paradise with the poverty of the inhabitants of Sutton.

But who was I to talk? I came of the wealthy Freine family. That was why I was here. My kinsman Walter de Freine, of Freen's Court, had asked the prior to make me a canon of St. Guthlac's. Then I would be able to preach in the two Sutton churches, St. Nicholas and St. Michael's.

'Master de Freine,' the young monk interrupted my thoughts, 'the prior suggests you have time for prayers in the chapel before he sees you.'

I gazed up at the lofty roof. The chapel was a melancholy place but I was not humbled even after confessing my sins in Latin. The prior could hardly refuse Sir Walter's request for he owed him a favour. Hadn't Sir Walter given our chapel of St. Nicholas to St. Guthlac's when I was just a boy? The poor man was grief-stricken by the death of his wife, Albreda, so he had handed over his chapel in return for prayers for her soul.

As for St. Michael's, St. Guthlac's took that over before I was born. My mother told me how the monks laid hands on the key and bells, a custom which established their right of ownership.

Now St. Michael and St. Nicholas were going to have a priest of their own—one who could actually speak their language.

'Preach in English?' exclaimed the prior. 'That hardly does justice to the word of God! No doubt you will write your sermons in Latin and translate as you deliver them. Sir Walter tells me you're not only learned in the Latin tongue, but also something of a poet.'

I doubted whether he had heard my poems read. Even my old friend Giraldus Cambrensis constantly missed my recitations! Anyway I wrote my poems in Norman French for the benefit of castle and court—not in Latin, the language of study.

Fortunately the prior didn't pursue the matter. I was dismissed with a blessing and dispatched to cure and preach to the three hundred or so souls of Sutton.

My parishioners were humble peasants and tradesmen. They didn't understand the Latin mass but were awed by the strange and wonderful words. They would kneel on the stone floor of the nave and watch me performing Mass at the altar in the chancel where they were not allowed. What they knew of heaven and hell they gleaned from statues and colourful wall paintings in the church.

How amazed they were when I described the joys of heaven and torments of hell in their own language. The Ten Commandments which they had learnt by heart in Latin suddenly meant something.

Inspired with thoughts of the life to come, they returned to their cramped and smelly huts.

They were very poor, my people. So were my churches. Their combined income was consistently below £12. Out of that came £1 6s. 8d. of tax paid annually to the king. Besides this, everyone had to give up a tenth of their produce to St. Guthlac's for the benefit of the Church. Of that I was allowed to keep about a quarter for the parish to help the poor, sick and elderly.

Even those who couldn't afford it paid their tithes without complaint. Some, I know, feared me as they feared the lord of the manor who could have them flogged if they misbehaved. I prefer to think, however, that they paid their tithes willingly as the result of my sermons. 'Lay not up for yourselves treasures on earth and trust not in riches' were popular themes of mine.

Yet evil spirits and ignorance persistently afflicted my congregation. I despaired of ever educating them.

Then Adam and Joseph came to me. They wanted to learn Latin, they told me, so that they could know more about God. I taught them in the church by candlelight after they had laboured all day in the fields. Adam was working in Westfield and Joseph in Lowerfield. They were good boys, never entering the church without washing their feet in the brook first. After a year of study I had trained them to help with church services. In time my pupils would become priests, I prayed.

Then came the time when Hereford gained its charter from Richard I. Forty marks of silver the city paid for its charter—but alas, that was only part of the cost. The king had only one aim: to raise cash to ferry his army to the Holy Land and drive Saladin and the Turks from Jerusalem. He was selling everything he had: state offices, lordships, earldoms, sheriffdoms, farms, lands. 'I would sell the city of London,' he declared, 'if only I could find a buyer.'

The king was a committed Christian but I doubted whether he was a wise one. Adam and Joseph had no such reservations. They were filled with admiration for the king who had killed a lion single-handed and eaten its heart raw! Yes, the Lionheart had won the hearts of my devout pupils and when the time came for their next lesson, I waited in vain in the church. They had left Sutton to join the Third Crusade. I was never to see Joseph again.

Adam did return, three years later. An older Adam, pale from intermittent fever. The Crusade had failed but he was still fiercely loyal to the king. He wouldn't speak of Joseph or of the battle horrors he had witnessed. Instead he told me stories he had heard about St. George.

I turned Adam's stories into a poem. I became obsessed by the martyrdom of George. I wrote of his horrible torture and the three deaths he died. Twice he was miraculously restored to life, but on the third occasion he passed into the joyous and permanent state of Paradise.

I realised it wasn't St. George I was writing about, God forgive me, it was Joseph. 'St. George teaches us,' I told my congregation, 'that Christian soldiers cannot die'. I even read my poem in French from the pulpit.

> La nus doinst le joie fine
> Qui nul jour de l'an ne fine,
> Joie et permenable vie,
> Amen! Amen! Chescun die!

Time heals; Adam never became a priest but I appointed him as local exorciser. I wrote more poetry about the uncertainty of fortune and the consolation to be found in divine philosophy. I became known as the Rhyming Canon and when I needed intellectual stimulus, I would visit my brother canons in the city of Hereford.

I was content with my aged muse. Not so my old friend, Giraldus Cambrensis. He was disappointed because the Archbishop of Canterbury had appointed someone else to be Bishop of St. David's, even though the clergy of that diocese had elected Giraldus.

'Come to our city,' I wrote to him, 'where there are men who love learning, and take the foremost place amongst us. The whole city will bow and be your slave. There are philosophers here, in you only will be their glory; the people of the city also will glory in you alone. If they have not yet made you a bishop, you will find peace and rest, the opportunity to serve God and to win the glory that never fades.'

The glory that never fades. Surely that must also belong to Joseph.

John Birch of Weobley

look up at Weobley's timbered houses. They are at it again: leaning forward to eavesdrop and conspire. 'Here's Colonel Birch,' they whisper, 'the Roundhead Commander who later turned Royalist!'

'It's easy to be wise after the event,' I retaliate. 'Parliaments will always need the restraint of kings. That was something I had to learn.'

Because of my capture of their city, Hereford folk are suspicious of me. But there's no need, for I'm a God-fearing man.

I admit I came here first because I didn't want to be stuck down in Bristol in 1645. I was too ambitious to stay on the provincial sidelines during the Civil War and I wanted more than the Governorships of Bristol and Bath, but to achieve my aim of entering politics and gain notice, I needed a sensational military success. Where better to make a mark than in Herefordshire—one of the bastions of Royalist support throughout the Civil War. Hereford reckoned without John Birch!

Influential friends in London soon secured me a commission to 'distress the city of Hereford' with an army of some 1,800 horse and foot. I took my troops to Gloucester where I conferred with Governor Morgan and Sir John Bridges, who weren't optimistic. 'To attack Hereford in mid-winter is foolhardy,' declared Sir John, 'the roads out there are poor and the villages newly ransacked, food is scarce and the population hostile.'

I admitted I had never been to Hereford and needed to see for myself. Sir John agreed to accompany me—to prove his point. So we made a secret visit to a remote farm near Ledbury where we met two ex-Royalist captains, eager to furnish us with information.

'Hereford's garrison is around 1,500 strong, and at night a strict guard is kept,' Captain Alderne told me, 'but in the morning, after the gates are opened, the soldiers go drinking and leave only ten or so on guard.'

'And the officers?'

'Sleeping off the all-night drinking and gambling session,' chuckled Captain Howarth.

To capture the city I must know its routine, so I was particularly interested to learn that each morning peasants arrived from nearby villages to break the ice in the city ditch, while others brought cartloads of straw and wood into the city. I also discovered that there were two places near Byster's Gate where I could hide my forces; a few could be concealed in the ruins of St. Guthlac's Priory, and the others in a convenient hollow, known as Scots Hole.

'Byster's Gate is my way into Hereford,' I muttered to myself and returned to Gloucester to my men, whom I promptly marched to Ledbury.

The following night we set off for Hereford—what an endurance test! The snow was so deep in places it almost buried my foot soldiers. We came within four miles of Hereford but I didn't intend attacking that day: I had come to gauge the lie of the land and to set a trap. 'We shall return to Gloucester and await fairer conditions,' I declared loudly, knowing there were spies abroad.

In fact we returned to Ledbury and were back the next night. My plan worked well, thanks to Almighty God who provided the heavy

frost and covering of snow. Who could believe that a whole army could move so silently through so many villages without a single dog barking? It was a miracle, no less. By morning I had all my men concealed in Scots Hole and St. Guthlac's Priory.

Six of my men were disguised as peasants, with pick-axes and shovels, another had assumed the role of constable and held a false warrant. For two hours we waited in the bitter cold of the Priory ruins, and then at last the gates were opened and we heard the creaking of the drawbridge being lowered.

My rustics and their constable went forward; the officer studied their warrant. For literally one minute my brave 'peasants' held the gate and then my army poured in. Hereford fell in half an hour, with a loss of only ten men.

Yes, I took the city without unnecessary loss of civilian life and immediately checked the plundering of my victorious troops.

Of course, I didn't expect gratitude, but frankly I was more unpopular in Hereford than I had expected. 'We are all cousins in Herefordshire' they say and it's a fact! Strangers can be unwelcome! Even the dean abused my regiment in his sermon, and I was forced to place the city under martial law.

Ironically I felt secure and at home, for Hereford was remote from the excesses of Cromwell's stern Protectorate. By the time news of the King's execution (God forgive us all) reached Hereford, its distressing details had misted into legend.

I kept 'my' head down and set about feathering my own nest, availing myself of the glut of church property on the market—no less than five episcopal manors and the bishop's palace! But what the Lord giveth with one hand, he taketh away with the other for, after the Restoration, bishops were in vogue once more and the king forced me to restore the episcopal manors and the palace to the Bishop of Hereford. Still, God looks after his own, and being on the Council of State that recalled Charles II to England in 1660, my reward was the post of Auditor of the Excise.

I needed somewhere to live, now that my manors had been reclaimed and, having taken to the county, I looked for a borough which I could represent as its M.P., and thought of Weobley. Here was my opportunity to ensure political independence in the House of Commons, and at the same time buy a large county property on

the village outskirts. Yes, I would buy the Garnstone estate and win one of the two Weobley seats in Parliament.

Weobley was a pocket borough. The inhabitants had no choice but to elect their landowner as Member of Parliament. Not, mind you, that I left anything to chance for they didn't trust me, though they daren't say so—I was the man who had captured Hereford and terrorised the county in the name of Parliament. I had to use my skill in oratory and appeal to their Royalist sympathies. 'Greetings to you, in the name of our gracious Majesty King Charles II,' I began, 'I know you served his father well when he sought shelter in Weobley after the Battle of Naseby.'

No response. These folk don't really care about King or Parliament, I thought. They're too poor. Bribery is the answer, for one glance at their half-timbered cottages had told me all I wanted to know—the thatch was rotting and the walls were rat-infested.

'Your cottages shall be repaired,' I continued. 'My thatchers, builders and rat-catchers will come down from Garnstone. You can always count on your Member of Parliament to look after you.'

They nodded in agreement. One man was even bold enough to seize my hand. I was Weobley's M.P. from that moment.

I had made a bold promise. Too bold, perhaps, for I had my own house to put in order. I obtained Garnstone Castle cheaply, for £1,500, in 1661. It was imposing but Roger Vaughan, who sold it to me, had let it fall into disrepair.

'It's a ruin, John,' gasped my wife, Alice. 'It's no better than the ruined Norman castle in the village.'

'It'll be a gentle habitation in no time, my dear,' I replied with my usual characteristic optimism.

'It'll take you all of twenty years. I shall never see it finished,' she muttered.

I looked at her pale face and I knew she was right, but I had dreams for Garnstone. As the years went by, I bought up surrounding farms—even the land between my estate and the centre of Weobley. I dreamt of a road linking Garnstone with Weobley's main street.

Alice settled at Garnstone despite her misgivings. As for the children, they loved it. John and Samuel made friends with local boys. They prevailed on me to let them attend the newly built grammar school, but I was reluctant for I had employed an excellent master to teach my children at home.

Yet I never forgot my own origins. I remembered my mother's face when I left my Manchester home at eighteen—to seek my fortune. I was severely wounded when the Royalists attacked Bristol and the surgeons left me for dead. 'No good wasting precious dressings on him,' they said. Then the weather turned extremely cold and congealed the flow of blood.

'Go to school, my sons,' I told them, 'and God go with you!'

Alas, I misjudged. That grammar school might look just like any other timber-framed Herefordshire house, but it wasn't. How was I to know that within those walls lurked the Devil? One day, while the master was upstairs in his chamber, the boys, in the big classroom downstairs, read the books he had left on his desk. They learnt about the 'Old Un' and how to raise him. The Devil took over. An ear-splitting noise rocked the foundations and objects were lifted into the air. I sent an exorcist to the school as soon as I heard, and promptly dismissed the master for leaving his pupils alone with such sacrilegious literature. The teacher whom I had originally hired to educate my sons at Garnstone was appointed instead.

Satanic dallying wasn't restricted to the school. I have myself caught folk walking round the preaching cross in the churchyard at midnight saying the Lord's Prayer backwards—to conjure the Devil. 'You whoreson rogues!' I yelled and they ran like the wind! They feared the Birch more than the Devil!

As principal landowner I had to be conscious of my responsibilities to the community, especially to the church. My family and I attended regularly, sitting in the Chapel of St. Nicholas on the south of the nave.

> Poor Weobley, proud people
> Low church, high steeple

So goes the saying. But the lofty spire fell with its cross in the great storm of 1640. I arranged for it to be replaced in 1675, but it was an expensive job, even though it was twenty feet shorter than the original!

I rebuilt and repaired the chancel too—at the request of Bishop Croft who, as dean, had previously attacked my soldiers from his pulpit in the cathedral. My willing response was proof that I had turned my sword into a ploughshare.

I told him how the glory of Nature surveyed from the high ridge of Garnstone banishes all thoughts of war. But what I didn't tell him was that Garnstone with its orchards and hopyards is more than a Garden of Eden: it's my retreat! I campaign for religious toleration at Westminster, and when the House of Commons turns hostile, I can escape to Weobley. No-one is likely to pursue me to a place where the roads become impassable after autumn rains until the following spring!

At such times local morale is bolstered by our famous Weobley Ale. But cider is becoming increasingly popular, which proved an opportunity I couldn't miss. Just wait till they tasted cider in London! So I promptly leased 55 acres in Hyde Park for the purpose of planting cider apple trees.

Charles II was eager to share in my enterprise so I agreed to deliver half the annual crop to the Palace. Unfortunately the Dutch War intervened in 1665—before the orchard could be planted and when the king needed cash not apples. I busied myself in the House of Commons where I came up with the original idea of a poll-tax 'for charging all people that pay no land tax.'

I liked the king. I believe King Charles was sincerely devoted to the Church of England and that he genuinely wanted religious freedom for his subjects. His brother and heir was another matter! James was a Catholic through and through. All were agreed in Parliament that he should be excluded from the throne, as the Protestant religion could no more be preserved by a popish successor than water could be kept cold in a hot pot!

What a shock when King Charles dissolved Parliament to prevent our excluding James from the throne. How glad I was then to be able to retreat to Weobley where I devoted my time to performing my duties as chief landowner. I exchanged small parcels of land with my neighbours and it became a pleasure to consolidate my holdings and enclose them. I worked extremely hard at improving my estate and I was sorry that Alice never lived to see the improvements.

But a positive approach was now necessary and I used the opportunity to marry again—a Weobley girl. She's no beauty, but she looks after me well.

James II only survived on the throne for three years and I was still looking to the future, not just for my estate and Weobley, but also for England. Aged 73, I was fit enough to ride out to meet William of Orange who had just landed on the south coast of England and was very pleased to see me. The benefit of my experience may have been initially lost on him but I'm sure he will value it in retrospect. I thank God that I have lived to see a constitutional sovereign receive the crown from the hands of Parliament. I've fought for that with words and the sword, all my life. Long live William III!

What saddens me, though, is that people have become so selfish. Where is the religious fervour of yesterday? Self-interest and materialism are the order of today. A thousand attended church last Sunday, yet only thirty received the sacrament. He that is unworthy of one is unfit for the other.

All I want now is to be buried in Weobley Church, as near my son Thomas as possible. I wanted so desperately to establish a family line for Garnstone—but in my old age, I am denied a male heir. My only surviving son has failed to produce one.

I am flesh and therefore must perish, but I must have a lifesize replica of me in marble. It shall stand forever on the right hand of God's altar at Weobley. They may not heed the whispering eaves of Weobley's leaning houses, but woe betide those who misread the message in the marble eyes of Colonel Birch: kings need the restraint of Parliament, but Parliaments also need the restraint of kings!

Francis Godwin of Whitbourne

am and therefore you will be,' said my father. I knew what would come next: the family motto: Win God-Win All!

Yes, father was, and therefore I am, a bishop. Reluctantly I had to acknowledge that the Church was the only road for a man of learning. And that is what I am. Had I come from a different parentage perhaps I would have become a valiant sea-dog like Drake, for 'neath my composed countenance lies a frustrated explorer who wants to make history, not write it. Oh yes, I've had my royal recognition alright, but for a dull old catalogue of the bishops of England with a short history of their lives. It hardly compares with sailing round the world!

Still, it gained me a bishopric I suppose. Or did the good old queen make me Bishop of Llandaff before she died, out of affection for my father? No matter, from there I came to Hereford.

And what is Hereford but a collection of taverns and cider-sellers? Oh, I know we must have our cider, it's our staple drink for young and old alike, but an excess leads to quarrelling, duelling and untimely death. Not what I intend for my sons; they must live, hawk and hunt till I can provide them with livings. My wife, though old, is even now big-bellied with child and fears the pestilence that ravages the towns. Of our daughters, Alice is already betrothed and shall be married soon, God willing. But what of my needs—above all, I desire peace and quiet to write, undistracted by episcopal affairs.

I found it eventually at Whitbourne, or White Stream, about as far away from my cathedral as I could get and ironically much closer to my brother bishop's seat at Worcester, barely ten miles away as compared to twenty from Hereford! My summer palace as it was termed could be my winter palace too. I let it be known how treacherous the road is. 'Very difficult after heavy rain,' I warn prospective visitors, 'as the River Teme often floods this extreme part of Herefordshire, whilst in fine weather the stones have lamed many horses. Then, too, the wind lifts the dry soil and blows it in the faces of travellers.'

If they still feel obliged to visit me, on their heads be it! I can offer accommodation for persons of note and other folk can put up at the inn, which is just by the entrance to both the church and my palace.

What's to prevent me from conducting my diocesan affairs from here? My predecessors, God bless them, created a precedent by holding ordinations here, either in the Manor Chapel or in Whitbourne Church. That church isn't so much the centre of the village as a starting point for a straggle of cottages following the Whitbourne Brook into the shelter of wooded hills. But there's ample mature timber hereabouts which has provided Whitbourne with quality timber-framed houses. As for my court, despite its eleven chimneys, it's a veritable castle with its moat and drawbridge. Yes, at Whitbourne I can barricade myself against the world and justify my seclusion by writing more learned books.

Yet what is learning but other men's ideas? Must I accept because I cannot know, that God's universe is finite? I am informed that it has ten revolving spheres, decreasing in size like toy boxes

and fitting inside each other. Can it be so? I long to fly into space and prove it wrong.

Meanwhile, History fetters my pen which is the slave of duty. What dull stuff I write, not that which dreams are made of. How I envy that popular Stratford playwright whose work is fired with imagination.

But surely I too have time to dream? I often do as I stroll in the grounds of my castle, The Park as it's known, where my vineyard climbs over what looks like a Roman amphitheatre. Winter approaches but my southern bank is still patterned with clusters of brittle vine. For all I know or dream, imperious Caractacus, turned to clay, could lie beneath my shoe. And I too am of the earth, unable to soar up into the heavens to explore the skies like those swallows skimming over the moat. At night I have mistaken them for bats in the flame of my steward's torch, whilst now they haunt me as I lie alone in my four poster as my wife prepares for another lying-in in our second best bed in a room along the corridor. The mid-wife is with her but her time is not yet come. Pray God she may be delivered of a healthy child.

Would that the embroidered hangings round my bed did not seem like a shroud, yet there is light in the darkness: the moon will not be hidden. I worship its light, tantalised by its eternal perfection. Its hypnotic eye compels me. A strange sensation flows through my limbs and it's then that I know the moon is my destiny.

But how to reach it? I have no wings so I must be borne on those of birds. I imagine I'm standing on a hill waving a cloth to summon fifty wild swans trained to obey that signal. Tonight sees their ultimate test as they are tethered to pulleys to take the strain. They have already carried a lamb in their harness, but now it is my turn.

There is a rush of air beneath my feet as I feel myself lifted off the ground. For eleven days and nights I'm whirled violently through the air, asleep on a bed of down. My swans reach a height at which they remain unmovable as if they are sitting on so many perches—only our globe possesses that secret property which draws weights down to the surface. And so I migrate effortlessly to my other world, the moon.

As I awake I see it glowing before me in natural colours so unlike the lurid blue of our Earth, which lies far below. As the

swans lower me I gaze on a mighty sea besprinkled with islands. I land on one and unhitch my harness. What amazing trees! Three times as high as ours with trunks five times as thick. With a great fluttering my swans swoop onto a gigantic green shrub and greedily eat its leaves. Seized with ravenous hunger, I thrust a leaf between my teeth. It's incredibly delicious and I can't stop eating until I suddenly realise I'm being watched.

My eyes won't focus properly but I'm aware of tall shadows, graceful giants clad in glowing lunar cloth. But fear grips me and I fall to my knees shouting, 'God help me!'

They immediately kneel too, in a circle round me. Instantly I know I have nothing to fear. Evil is unknown on the moon. It only exists in my mind. The tallest shadow takes me by the hand, raising me into the air like a toy so that I can walk with the moon folk fifty or sixty feet above the ground. They lead me into a building so lofty and beautiful that it makes our highest cathedral seem no more than a cottage.

My eyes cannot cope with the glory of the place and the beauty of its people. The women are so beautiful—I can't help thinking my wife is a grotesque pygmy by comparison! Voluptuous breasts in voluminous glowing gowns cloud the sky. Lust overpowers me and I stretch every limb that I might reach the soft clouds.

Thunderous words break from the sky, shaking the ground, 'A man having once known a woman must never desire another. We condemn you to ....'

A giant axe eclipses the glowing clouds. Are they going to execute me? Inexorably it seems, I watch the axe descend. I can't scream, I can't move.

I feel disorientated as though my head no longer belongs to me. 'Ridiculous!' I say to myself as I part the bed curtains and put my feet tentatively on the floor. How heavy is the jug on the washstand. Shaking, I pour water into the basin. Then I have the courage to face the new glass mirror by the window. Yes, I'm still in one piece, though my face is white and my beard ruffled. Let it be a normal day, just to go to the church to celebrate Mass and pray for my wife's safe delivery, and thence to my study.

Yet reminders of execution are everywhere from the Norman head that peers from the fourteenth century church tower to the dedication of the church itself, to John the Baptist. Does it all bode ill for my unborn child?

The bells must ring to avert the evil. I must be positive. I don my ancient cope though it isn't a saint's day, but what of that? Every

148

day is a celebration of life in this world. My obsessive urge to conquer space must be controlled.

How rich is the red velvet of my cope! Could lunar colours be more resplendent? A servant girl interrupts my reverie. 'Come quickly my lord, my lady is delivered!'

I stand at the door of my wife's bedchamber. What dreadful sight awaits me? After that dream, can the baby really be normal? It's difficult to tell from the bloodstained screaming scrap which lies between my wife's legs. I must look, I must face it, for deformed or not it is my child. The midwife now holds it up. 'You have another son, my lord,' she declares. I hold my breath and scrutinise the child. Praise God, my son is whole.

Back in my study I take up my pen. I must face my destiny. No more learned treatises, instead I must take charge of the moon world. No moon men shall execute Francis Godwin—exile to Earth shall be the ultimate punishment. However, I shall invent a new herb (just to be on the safe side) that will join a man's severed head to his carcass again, so that the wounded party shall become perfectly whole in a few hours. My dream shall be realised at least on paper. My imagination shall create Utopia.

I begin to feel heavy and deliver myself to sleep, the sister of Death. On awaking, I am unbelievably fresh, nimble and vigorous. I must settle myself immediately to learning the Moon language, which is the same throughout all the regions of the Moon, for war cannot exist where there is understanding. Love surrounds me and I am overwhelmed by the abundant happiness of the place. I want to stay forever, but my swans are ailing and if I am ever to return I must soon face the danger of the return voyage. I fasten my harness and grip it tightly as my swans lift me into the air. I open my eyes—I have returned safely. The story shall be my masterpiece, though I will not show it to my contemporaries for fear they should laugh at my dreams. Indeed, in my writings I shall make the return to Earth happen on the far side of the world. My reputation rests, after all, on my learned histories—such dull stuff.

Meanwhile I shall dream, and wonder whether man will ever reach the moon. No matter, I, Francis Godwin, went there first, in my dreams and by my pen.

Wulviva of Woolhope

ho would be the younger sister of Godiva? She was not only the most beautiful but also the most saintly woman of our day. I, Wulviva, was forever in her shadow.

I imagine her amidst her bower-maidens in her husband's fine Danish hall at Bourne, where her husband Earl Leofric, Lord of Bourne and all Mercia, worshipped her. Even the late King Canute had adored her, but now the earls Leofric and Godwin were the most powerful men in England. Yet Leofric had my sister to contend with.

I could never recall her acclaimed 'noble deed' in Coventry without shame. Leofric was determined that every citizen of the town, however poor, should pay his heavy taxes—Godiva remonstrated with him in vain. She offered him all her precious stones instead, but he wouldn't be persuaded, so she offered what he treasured beyond all else—her naked body. She would ride, she said, naked through the streets of Coventry to save its citizens from taxation. He was titillated by the thought, I know it. Why else would he let her do it? He wanted to see her bare white legs astride her steed, but the thought of other men's eyes on her soft supple flesh appalled him. An edict was issued: everyone was to stay indoors behind closed shutters. Only Leofric would see Godiva ride. They all obeyed, except for one called Tom who bored a hole through his wall so he could have just a peep. He was so enraptured by the sight of her breasts, veiled by her golden hair but rising and falling voluptuously in rhythmic motion with her horse, that he had to tell. In no time the news reached the court. In his rage, Leofric personally gouged out the man's eyes with a red hot iron. My sister wept at the fellow's agony and prayed for him throughout the ensuing night, kneeling on the cold stone of the chapel floor. I know because I prayed beside her.

Every day we used to read the psalter through, and during Lent we'd watch in the church, saying a triple Matins—one for the Trinity, one for St. Mary and one for the Cross. St. Mary, may God forgive me, seemed less of a virgin than my sister—even though she had born Leofric a son. We prayed together less after the Coventry episode. She was always off on her travels round England, feeding thirteen poor folk at her own expense wherever she went and enriching numberless monasteries including Leominster, Wenlock, Chester, Worcester and Evesham. What's more, Archbishop Ethelnoth presented her with a priceless holy relic for her favourite monastery, the one she founded in Coventry.

And what of me? What of Wulviva? You may well ask. Estates had I none—save one manor, and even that I owned jointly with Godiva, though she gave me a free hand in its running.

We called it a Hope, as it was a small enclosed valley running up to the hills. Yes, my manor, Wulviva's Hope, is in a beautiful elevated valley, cradled amidst dome-shaped thickly wooded hills. How I love to clamber up the sloping pastures to the east of the village where masses of wild daffodils grow in the Spring. The edges of the woods abound with primroses and cowslips and the woodlands grow misty with bluebells.

Up the track from my manor house is the common, generally known as 'the Wastes'. There my villagers pasture their cattle,

151

sheep, goats, swine and geese. My priest has more than his fair share of pasture: indeed he's known for bargaining at market against his fellows in the hope of making a good profit. Fortunately, though, it's a large common with sufficient pasture. With other villages the Wastes become overcharged by the number of cattle put on them and hardship arises.

My lands are extensive, encompassing around 1,500 acres. The village itself, however, consisting of the manor house with the priest's house and a handful of cottages clustered round it, is small by comparison. Other cottagers live around the common, two even on the brink of the woods.

I love the woods—especially Haugh Wood which lies across the common to the west of the village. The priest says the Evil One lives there, in the shape of a dragon. 'Don't ride there, my lady,' he warns, 'you will surely fall into the Devil's power.'

I ride there just the same with Gerland, my faithful hound, running beside me. The secrets of this forest are mine alone. Godiva has never ridden here. Only Wulviva dares ignore the warnings of the priest. And it is in these woods that I see death and rebirth illustrated far more potently than in his sermons. A dead pine needle moves and reveals a minute green shoot springing out of the damp soil. Last year's brittle hard spiky bracken makes way for this year's hairy green fronds, then the gorse's yellow blossom brings out the bees.

Those are the images I carry with me to Mass in the little chapel that forms part of my house. My cottagers, uncomfortable in their best clothes, huddle together at the back; my household sit behind me at the front. The priest always uses the occasion to preach on the seven deadly sins, warning us that we would pay in purgatory unless we were truly penitent and shriven. In vain I have confessed and received absolution many times, but still envy of Godiva eats into my soul.

Only in Haugh Wood am I free of it; Gerland is released too, chasing rabbits through the undergrowth and occasionally emerging with one in his mouth. 'Drop it, Gerland!' I order and he does so. He doesn't hurt it as his mouth is soft. The rabbit is initially motionless, startled by its deliverance, before it recovers and its white tail bobs into the trees.

One day, the day that changed my life, Gerland caught a baby rabbit that didn't run away. Believing it was hurt I dismounted. Suddenly a deafening roar rose from the earth; it moved the ground and shook the trees. My terrified horse bolted. So loud was the rumbling that I never heard the crack as the tree fell. I sank down, unconscious on the wet grass.

In that strange realm between life and death, I overheard two voices talking. The first was loud and dogmatic. In it I recognized the voice of my priest declaring: 'Envy is the Devil's work. The soul of Wulviva is doomed! Let her beware the mouth of Hell!'

The other was a softer voice, yet firm. 'Guilt only feeds envy. Let Wulviva find her own way to Heaven, and judge not lest ...'

I came to and found Gerland's warm rough tongue licking my face. I opened my eyes to discover my horse had fled; trees lay across the track but the forest was still—eerily silent.

Slowly I picked my way through the fallen trees and frantic undergrowth until I came to the common. There I was met by the priest and several cottagers, one of whom was leading my horse.

'Praise God you are safe, my lady! We thought the dragon had devoured you. We heard it roaring in the forest.'

'There is no dragon, priest!' I heard myself say. My voice sounded strange, soft yet firm. 'It was the earthquake you heard.'

'Alas no, my lady, the Devil lurks yonder in the form of a serpent-dragon.' My peasants nodded, they had accepted the priest's version of everything since birth. I smiled. I wasn't afraid of him anymore. In future I would trust my own judgment.

It was time my cottagers had their own church and a priest who wouldn't blackmail them with threats of purgatory—if only I could find one. The Bishop of Hereford might know such a man—so I would arrange with my sister to gift the manor to Hereford Cathedral. The cathedral would be patrons of the church, a church dedicated to St. George, for was not he a dragon-slayer?

As for Godiva, pour soul, all I was to feel for her in future was sisterly compassion. Her son, Hereward, the apple of her eye and a brave rebel, was to die prematurely—his head sliced off by a Norman sword. As for her famous ride, posterity would turn it into ribald humour. But my memorial would be a beautiful village perched amongst wooded hills—Wulviva's Hope.

Historical Background & Sources

Abbeydore

The Cistercian Abbey at Dore was founded in 1147, but the first buildings must have been temporary, the rebuilding of the church starting about 1175-80 and continuing throughout the twelfth and thirteenth centuries. Following the Dissolution, the abbey was restored by John Scudamore in the seventeenth century.

Little is known of Dore's history in the twelfth century, a time when its spiritual and economic life would have been most active. The first date of any significance is 1198 when Giraldus Cambrensis wrote disparagingly of the monastery and its abbots.

The abbey was consecrated in 1275 by Thomas Cantilupe, Bishop of Hereford, at the risk of his life since the bishop of St. David's backed his own claim to the abbey with a show of military force, supported by Tregoz who was either Cantilupe's brother-in-law or nephew.

Butler, Lionel and Given-Wilson, Chris *Medieval Monasteries of Great Britain*

Coppack, Glyn *Abbeys and Priories*
Gibson, Matthew *A View of the Ancient and Present State of the Churches of Dor, Home-Lacy and Hempsted*
Sledmere, Edwin *Abbey Dore*
Unstead, R.J. *Monasteries*
Williams, D.H. *Abbey Dore* Monmouthshire Antiquary, Vol 2 pt 2 1966

Bacton

Bacton was the home of Blanche Parry (1506-1589) who served Queen Elizabeth for about 50 years. She was granted full charge of the infant princess and became Chief Gentlewoman of the Bedchamber until, frail and blind, she died at the age of 82. As 'surrogate mother' and lifelong friend, she probably knew more about Elizabeth than anyone else.

Blanche's affection for her birthplace never waned. It is said her 'heart' or seat of emotion (generally assumed to be her bowels) is buried at Bacton, whilst her will contained bequests to the village. An impressive stone monument in St. Faith's Church, Bacton, features Queen Elizabeth with her friend and confidant. On the north wall hangs a framed piece of Blanche's embroidery, said to be part of one of her Court dresses. It was later cut up to serve as an altar frontal.

Bradford, Charles A. *Elizabeth's Gentlewoman*
Hibbert, Christopher *The Virgin Queen*

Brockhampton

This village is famous for its thatched church designed by Lethaby, who epitomised the Arts and Crafts Movement. All Saints was built in 1901-2 by Alice Foster in memory of her American parents, who had bought Brockhampton Court and given it to Alice as a wedding present. Brockhampton Court stands in six acres of its own grounds and appears to have hardly altered since Alice Foster's day, although it has since been converted into an hotel.

Ellis, A.H. *All Saints Church, Brockhampton* (Research Paper
            F003517X)
The Architects Journal, 15 Aug 1990
Brockhampton Court Hotel prospectus

Clifford

Jane Clifford was the beautiful, ill-fated mistress of Henry II, who called her the Rose of the World, or Rosa Mundi. It is thought that Henry first met her when he came to subdue the unruly marcher lords in 1153.

She had two sons by the king: William, surnamed 'Longspée' and Geoffrey. Her intimacy with Henry appears to have lasted twenty years.

Tradition claims that Henry built a labyrinth at Woodstock to protect Rosamund from his jealous queen, Eleanor. The latter, however, attached a piece of thread to her husband's foot and so exposed her rival's hiding-place. She then confronted Rosamund with the choice of a dagger or poison. The cup carved on Rosamund's tomb at Godstow Nunnery where she was known and loved, suggests she was poisoned.

Clifford Castle is privately owned. For permission to view, ask at the white house at the end of the driveway.

Clifford, Arthur *Collecteana Cliffordiana* (1817)
Iron, Douglas *The Castle of Fair Rosamund* The Field, April 1955

Colwall

Elizabeth Barrett moved with her parents to Hope End when she was three. Her gift for writing poetry was encouraged by her dominant and fiercely protective father.

After a fall from her pony, when aged 15, her health suffered. Intellectual companionship, however, was provided by Hugh Stuart Boyd, a blind scholar of Greek who moved to Malvern in 1825.

Financial difficulties forced her widowed father to sell Hope End in 1832, when Elizabeth was 26. The family left for Sidmouth and thence Wimpole Street where she met and subsequently married Robert Browning, in spite of her father's opposition.

Barrett Browning, Elizabeth *The Barretts at Hope End, an early diary* (discovered 1961) John Murray, 1974
Watkins, Alfred *Elizabeth Barrett and Hope End*
The poems of Elizabeth Barrett Browning

Fownhope

Tom Spring was Fownhope's famous prizefighter. An ancient cider press marks his birthplace at Rudge End. He is featured in a mural at the Green Man, though he become landlord of Hereford's Booth

Hall. The annual walk commemorating the Fownhope Heart of Oak Friendly Society still takes place in the village on Oak Apple Day.

Butcher, Basil *County Heritage* Hereford County Life, Feb 1975
Gange, Edmund Fortescue *Fownhope Its Church & Its People*

Goodrich

Goodrich Castle almost certainly takes its name from Godric Mapson, who's parentage is unkown. He is mentioned as holding Hülle at the time of Domesday, it having been held by Taldus before 1066, in return for service to the king. It is mentioned as Godric's Castle in 1101-2, but the stone keep is unlikely to be pre-1100. Recent research by Copleston-Crow argues that Hülle is equivalent to the present parish of Goodrich.

Goodrich Castle was probably built by Godric to guard the 'Walecford' soon after the Welsh had been driven further west. Walford is a contraction of Walecford, the Welsh Ford, being the passage through the River Wye opposite Goodrich Castle, and which had been a thoroughfare between England and Wales since Roman Times. The Domesday Commissioners found Walecford to be part of the episcopal estate.

Clare, John D. *Knights in Armour*
Garmonsway, G.N. (trans) *The Anglo-Saxon Chronicle*
Moir, Preb. A.L. *Bishops of Hereford*
Radford, Raleigh *English Heritage Guide to Goodrich Castle*
Reade, Compton ed. *Memorials of Old Herefordshire*

Hardwicke

Henrietta Webb lived in Hardwicke Vicarage from 1865-1885. An accurate picture of the house and its contents can be formed from the auctioneer's list when the house was sold on the death of the Webbs in 1885.

Henrietta's husband, the Reverend Thomas Webb, known as The Father of Amateur Astronomy, was the author of the classic *Celestial Objects*. The couple had no children, but Henrietta's nieces, Helen (the 'fair Helen of Troy' of Kilvert's diary) and Louisa Wyatt, were frequent visitors.

Henrietta spent hours painting in watercolours. The drawing room door of the former Hardwicke Vicarage (now the Haven Guest House) is still covered in her designs, including a curious waterbird with a long beak.

Kilvert's Diary
Hardwicke Church publication for a Webb Weekend, November 1990

Hereford

Edith Oldecriste, wife of Robert, an ironmonger, recovered in Hereford Cathedral from being 'furiosa' (insane) on the Friday before Palm Sunday in 1287.

Her cure was esteemed a miracle, the first to be imputed to the then late Bishop Thomas Cantilupe, whose bones rested in the Lady Chapel shortly before they were moved to the new impressive north transept.

Alcohol, post-natal depression or a seizure were all possible explanations for Edith's condition as recorded by commissioners investigating Thomas Cantilupe's fitness for canonisation.

Numerous other miracles followed, bringing hundreds of pilgrims to the shrine of St. Thomas at Hereford—the only bishop of Hereford to have been made a saint.

Finucane, Ronald C. *Miracles & Pilgrims*
Jancey, Meryl Ed. *St. Thomas Cantilupe, Essays in his honour*
Johnson, Andrew and Punter, Stephen *Aspects of Herefordshire*
                                        Logaston Press, 1987
Ross, J.H. & Jancey, Meryl *The Miracles of St. Thomas of*
                         Hereford British Medical Journal,
                         Vol 295 Dec. 1987

Shoesmith, Ron *Hereford*
Strange, Richard *The Life of St. Thomas of Hereford*

Kilpeck

The muzzled bear is one of the eighty mysterious creatures on the continuous corbel table round the outside of Kilpeck Church. The church is famous for its unique sculpture carved inside and out by

Norman craftsmen who were clearly influenced by Celtic, Saxon and Scandinavian ideas—a strange blend of pagan and Christian heritage. Curiously, only two of the carvings on the corbels appear to have any religious significance—both depict the Holy Lamb of God.

The remains of Kilpeck Castle stand on a mound to the west of the church, commanding a fine view of the Black Mountains. After the Conquest, Kilpeck was given by William I to his kinsman William Fitz Norman, who built the castle. It was William's grandson, Hugh, by this time 'de Kilpeck', who built the church.

In the twelfth century, bears were believed to give birth to formless lumps which they then licked into shape.

Guide to Kilpeck Church and Castle
White, T.H. *The Book of Beasts* (translation from a Latin Bestiary of the twelfth century)

Kingsland

Merewald, King of Mercia, is said by some to be buried beneath the mound to the west of Kingsland Church. He was converted to Christianity by Edfride, a Northumbrian monk. The ancient manuscript *The Coming of Edfride and the Building of the Priory* tells how Edfride interpreted Merewald's dream.

Merewald's daughters became abbesses, the most notable being St. Milburga who founded the Benedictine Nunnery at Wenlock with her father's wealth. She is said to have been obeyed by the geese, which she commanded to keep away from her fields.

800 years later, during the Wars of the Roses, Edward Mortimer (later Edward IV) was preparing to fight the Lancastrain forces at Mortimer's Cross near Kingsland. In the early morning occurred a parhelion. His soldiers believed three suns were appearing through the mist, whilst Edward adroitly interpreted it as a sign from God, symbolising the Trinity, and so encouraged his troops to victory.

The Coming of Edfride and the Building of the Priory, written in the early days of Leominster Priory by one of the monks.
Beowulf
Reeves, N.C. *The Leon Valley*

Kington

Lady Margaret Hawkins came from the Vaughan family of Hergest Croft, just outside Kington. She became Lady of the Bedchamber to Queen Elizabeth and married Sir John Hawkins, the Elizabethan adventurer. She founded the Lady Hawkins School in Kington.

Fenn, R.W.D. & Sinclair, J.B. *The Parish Church of St. Mary's, Kington*
Hibbert, Christopher *The Virgin Queen*
The Will of Dame Margaret Hawkins etc. (kindly supplied by Lady Hawkins School)

Ledbury

Katherine Audley, born in 1272, was the eldest daughter of Sir John Giffard. She married Sir Nicholas Audley who died in 1299 (the same year as her father), leaving Katherine a wealthy widow with two young sons and a daughter, Ela. In 1309, Ela, sixteen and already a widow, hastily married James de Perers and was fined for doing so without licence. John Masefield tells how, at some unknown time, Ela and James de Perers took land and property at Ledbury from the bishop of Hereford. He suggests that Katherine may have moved to Ledbury and that her daughter wished to be near her. So Katherine was probably living at the Hazels, as the tradition says. Her husband's half-brother, Hugh de Audley, held a part at least of the Manor of Hasyll. In 1322/3, she became the recipient of a royal pension of £30 a year, granted to the 'recluse of Ledbury'. According to local tradition, it had been revealed to Katherine that she would only find a resting place where the bells should ring of their own accord. The bells of Ledbury had welcomed her in this way, for when her maid, Mabel, went to the belfry, she found it locked with no ringers there.

Katherine Audley is sometimes wrongly confused with Saint Katherine (Catherine) of Alexandria whose torture consisted of being broken on a wheel and in whose honour St. Katherine's Hospital was founded in Ledbury, in 1232. It was probably built on the site of the former Bishop's Palace, which had been moved to a new site beyond the Upper Cross in Ledbury. In 1230, the church's detached tower was built, replacing the bell-turret.

Farmer, David Hugh *The Oxford Book of Saints* OUP, 1978

Gavin Robinson, Miss S.F. *Ledbury Parish Church*

Hillaby, Joe *The Book of Ledbury* Barracuda Books, 1982

Johnson, Andrew & Punter, Stephen *Aspects of Herefordshire*
Logaston Press, 1987

Masefield, John *St. Katherine of Ledbury and other Ledbury papers*
Heinemann, 1951

Power, Ellen *Medieval Women* CUP, 1973

Leominster

The last recorded use of the ducking stool in England was at Leominster. In 1809, Jenny Pipes, alias Jane Corran, was paraded through the town on the stool and ducked in the water near Kenwater Bridge, by order of the magistrates. On her release from the stool, which can now be seen in the church, her first words were oaths and curses on the magistrates.

By 1804, Mrs. Betty Hughes, a labourer's wife at Kingsland, had become famous as a miracle worker. She was, however, declared an imposter and moved to Oxford to continue her 'cures'.

In 1808, the Reverend J. Williams, headmaster of Leominster's grammar school and curate of the Priory Church, published his *Leominster Guide*, which provides a useful and readable comment on Leominster society at the time of Jenny Pipes.

The most notable building in Leominster after the Priory Church is that of the Butter Market (known as the Buttercross where five ways once met), built by John Abel in 1634 and later used as the Town Hall. It has now been rebuilt just outside the town because in 1853 it was decided it stood in the way of new development.

Johnson, Andrew & Punter, Stephen *Aspects of Herefordshire*
Logaston Press, 1987

Malpas A. & T., Davis S. & A. *The Story of the Buttercross*
Leominster History Study
Group, 1993

Price, John *Historical & Topographical Account of Leominster*

Reeves, Norman C. *The Town in the Marches* Orpheus Press, 1973

Townsend, Rev. G.F. *Town & Borough of Leominster* S. Partridge,
Leominster & Hall & Co, London, 1862

Williams, Rev. Jonathan *Leominster Guide* 1808
Hereford Journal, Jan. - Dec. 1809

Mordiford

Until 1811 it was possible to see a portrait of the dragon on the west end of Mordiford Church. Tradition said it lived in Haugh Wood and came down daily to eat villagers and to drink from the river. It was finally killed by a man hidden in a cider barrel by the river, who shot it with an arrow through the bunghole, but was himself suffocated by its fumes.

The dragon probably symbolised the destructive power of the floods. In 1811, Pentaloe Brook swelled to unheard of proportions and swept away cottages, barns and a cider mill. The vicar subsequently had the dragon's picture removed from the church.

Buckley, S. *Mordiford and the Legendary Dragon* Herefordshire
Journey no. 21
McCaughreen, Geraldine *Fires Astonishment*

Orleton

In its church are two ancient Norman chests with iron strap hinges and a Norman font with nine tall figures round the bowl.

There is no direct evidence that Adam de Orleton (1277?-1345) was born in the village, but his relationship with the powerful Mortimers suggests that Adam may have been the son of one of Mortimer's tenants resident at Orleton.

In 1317, Adam was appointed bishop of Hereford by the Pope. Edward II opposed his appointment since Adam, who was clever and unscrupulous, was hand in glove with the king's bitter enemies, the Mortimers.

Both William and Henry de Orleton (possibly Adam's relatives) were Chief Stewards of Hereford in the reign of Edward II and their combined weight in Hereford may have been the reason for Isabella's choice of the city as her headquarters. Certainly, Adam supported her and Roger Mortimer, her lover, against the king and forced Edward to abdicate. Some sources maintain he was also responsible for the king's murder.

Hutchinson, John *Herefordshire Biographies*
Moir, Preb. A.L. *Bishops of Hereford*
The Register of Adam de Orleton

Ross-on-Wye

John Kyrle (1637-1724) lived in a house opposite the Market Hall, now converted into two shops. He was responsible for the town's first water supply, planted innumerable trees, restored the Wilton to Ross causeway, regularly distributed money to the poor and organized the appeal for the rebuilding of the church spire.

Many of his ideas were ahead of the times, for example the rehabilitation of prisoners and recognition of the need for a public park.

Eight years after his death, Alexander Pope immortalised his exemplary character in a poetical biography.

Perhaps Kyrle's liquid capital (probably in the form of hard cash in his pocket) was related to the obscure incident of his being arrested for highway robbery. Influential friends, however, are said to have quickly secured his bail.

Money-Kyrle, Rev. C.L. *Memorials of Old Herefordshire: John Kyrle and the Kyrle Family*
Ritchie, Carson *The Man of Ross* Country Quest, March 1992

Stretton Sugwas

Aquablanca, a foreigner from Savoy who spoke no English, was rewarded for his financial wizardry by Henry III with the bishopric of Hereford. One of his extravagant ideas was building Hereford Cathedral's north transept in a style similar to that of the new Westminster Abbey.

In Hereford he was unpopular. He fled from the city when a Welsh invasion was imminent and incurred the wrath of the king. So he returned, only to be seized by Sir Roger de Clifford and imprisoned in Eardisley Castle for three months. He is known to have stayed in his episcopal palace at Stretton Sugwas when his health was deteriorating, and where he made his will and is said to have died in 1268. An eighteenth century house (The Priory) now stands on the site of the episcopal manor house, its front garden including the original churchyard.

The Norman tympanum featuring Samson and the lion is preserved in the parish church.

Duncumb *Grimsworth Hundred*
Fenn, R.W.D. & Sinclair, J.B. *The Bishops of Hereford and their*
Palaces
Moir, Preb. A.L. *Bishops of Hereford*

Sutton St. Nicholas & Sutton St. Michael
Sutton is a parish with two churches. In 1131, Sutton St. Michael was given to the monks of St. Guthlac by its patron, Walter de le Turri. Between 1131-1148, Walter de Freine gave St. Nicholas to St. Guthlac's. According to S.H. Martin, 'We are right in identifying this Walter with the Walter of Moccas mentioned in the marginal note in Hereford Domesday.'

Simon de Freine (1146-1220) was one of the Freine family of Sutton. He was a canon of Hereford and is mentioned in the records of St. Guthlac's Priory as having held the 'tithes of Sutton St. Nicholas.' He was a friend of Giraldus Cambrensis and gained recognition as a poet towards the end of the twelfth century. His work included a poem on St. George, a legend brought back by the Crusaders.

Martin, S.H. *St. Guthlac's Priory & the City Churches*
Sutton St. Nicholas & Sutton St. Michael

Weobley
Colonel John Birch (1615-1691) was the Roundhead commander who captured Hereford by a surprise attack on Byster's Gate in the winter. He then became Member of Parliament for Weobley and bought Garnstone Castle which became his family home.

After quarrelling with Cromwell, he was instrumental in restoring Charles II to the throne. He lived to welcome William III, the constitutional monarch he desired and who received the crown from the hands of Parliament.

Birch's lifesize marble statue stands near the altar in Weobley Church.

Heath-Agnew, E. *From Roundhead to Royalist*
Shoesmith, Ron *Hereford*
Records from the Garnstone Estate (Hereford Record Office)

Whitbourne

Francis Godwin, Bishop of Hereford from 1617-1633, is buried in the church at Whitbourne. A rare embroidered medieval cope of red velvet hangs in the church and may have belonged to one of the bishops of Hereford whose manor house stood next door, where Whitbourne Court now stands, though still with the original moat.

Francis Godwin, a renowned scholar, wrote several learned books, but his famous work, *The Man in the Moone*, anticipates Jules Verne by 30 years and explores the theory of gravity, when his harnessed swans carry him to the moon. Here, he discovers a Utopia, whence anyone with evil qualities is expelled to earth. Sadly, he died with the manuscript still in his desk, never to know that his new kind of imaginative fiction would become a masterpiece.

Godwin, Francis *The Man in the Moone*
Williams, P. *A Bishop's Manor*

Woolhope

It is thought that Godiva and her sister Wulviva gave the manor of Woolhope to Hereford Cathedral in the eleventh century, the village taking its name from the less famous sister. A modern stained glass window in the church pictures both sisters. Wulviva has a dog and some rabbits at her feet. The church itself, St. George's, with its distant lych-gate, dates back to the twelfth century.

Godiva, wife of Leofric, Earl of Mercia, who died in 1057, was probably the mother of Hereward the Wake. Legend has it that Leofric promised to reduce the taxes of the people of Coventry if she rode naked through the streets at noon. Everyone retired indoors; 'Peeping Tom' bored a hole in the shutters and was struck blind.

County of Hereford Records: Greytree Hundred
Kingsley, Charles *Hereward the Wake*

General Bibliography

Bradfield, Nancy *Historical Costumes of England 1066-1968*
Harrap, 1958

Cannon, John & Griffiths, Ralph *Oxford Illustrated History of the
British Monarchy* OUP, 1988
Clapham, Sir John *A Concise Economic History of Britain* CUP,
1951
Cootes, R.J. *The Middle Ages* Longman, 1972

Duncumb, John *Collections Towards the History and Antiquities of
the County of Hereford* E.G. Wright, 1812

Farmer, David Hugh *The Oxford Dictionary of Saints* Clarendon
Press, 1978
Fraser, Antonia *The Lives of the Kings & Queens of England* Future
Publications, 1975

Herefordshire Federation of Women's Institutes *The Herefordshire
Village Book* Countryside Books, 1989
Howard-Jones, Jill *Secret Hereford* SB Publications, 1993

Johnson, Andrew & Punter, Stephen *Aspects of Herefordshire*
Logaston Press, 1987

Leather, Ella Mary *The Folklore of Herefordshire* Jakeman &
Carver, 1912

Myers, A.R. *England in the Late Midle Ages (1307-1536)* Penguin
Books, 1953

Palmer, Roy *The Folklore of Hereford & Worcester* Logaston
Press, 1992
Pevsner, Nikolaus *The Buildings of England: Herefordshire*
Penguin, 1963
Poole, Austin Lane *Domesday Book to Magna Carta (1087-1216)*
Clarendon Press, 1951
Powicke, Sir Maurice *The Thirteenth Century (1216-1307)* OUP
1961

Reade, Compton *Memorials of Old Herefordshire* 1904
Robinson, Rev. C.J. *A History of the Mansions and Manors of
Herefordshire* Scholar Press Ltd 1872

Sharpe, J.A. *Early Modern England A Social History 1550-1760*
Hodder & Stoughton 1987
Smith, George *The Dictionary of National Biography* OUP
Stenton, F.M. *Anglo-Saxon England* Clarendon Press 1943

Timmins, H.T. *Nooks and Corners of Herefordshire* Elliot Stock
1892
Thorn, Frank & Caroline (Ed.) *Domesday Book: Herefordshire*
Phillimore 1983

Unstead, R.J. *Travel by Road Through the Ages* Adam & Charles
Black 1959

Webster, Hutton *History of Civilisation Ancient & Medieval*
D.C. Heath & Co 1947
West, John & Margaret *A History of Herefordshire* Phillimore 1985
Woolhope Naturalists Field Club Transactions Est. 1851

Also from Logaston Press

The Folklore of Hereford & Worcester

by Roy Palmer. An up to date account covering places, people, churches, superstitions, the supernatural, witchcraft, work, song, stories, dance and the seasons. 288pp £8.95 ISBN 1 873827 02 4

Who killed Simon Dale? & other murder mysteries

by crime writer Kate Clarke. 14 true stories set in Herefordshire and the Welsh borders. Some cases are unsolved, in others doubt is cast on the verdict. 208pp £6.95 ISBN 1 873827 03 2

Monuments in the Landscape Vol 1
—A Guide to Prehistoric Sites in Herefordshire

by George Children and George Nash. The history, archaeology and anthropology of the county, with a detailed guide to the major sites, this book helps explain the settlement of Herefordshire and the progression from nomadism to the centralised hilltop settlements of the Iron Age. 144pp £6.95 ISBN 1 873827 09 1

Walks & More

by Andrew Johnson & Stephen Punter. A walking and guide book covering central Wales, Herefordshire, Worcestershire west of the Severn and southern Shropshire. 80 circular walks, a gazetteer to over 150 towns, villages and places of interest, plus chapters on history, agriculture, folklore, cider, beer, art and literature. 336pp paperback, illustrations, maps. £7.95 ISBN 0 9510242 6 4

Walks in Southern Powys & the Borders

by Andrew Johnson, 35 walks in an area of stunning beauty. Notes on the history plus several illustrations. £4.95 ISBN 0 9510242 8 0

Alfred Watkins—A Herefordshire Man

by Ron Shoesmith, Hereford city's archaeologist. Watkins, the author of *The Old Straight Track* which gave birth to ley lines, had many other varied interests—including brewing, photography and steam cars. Includes 80 photographs, many by Watkins. £5.95 ISBN 0 9510242 7 2